Jungle Doctor's

Casebook

Jungle Doctor's Casebook

by
Paul White

MOODY PRESS

CHICAGO

ISBN: 0-8024-4208-0
Printed in the United States of America

CONTENTS

To my friends
Audrey and Graham Delbridge

1

WAX

He was extremely tall and extremely miserable. He stood in front of me and shook his head dejectedly, his eyes on the ground.

I took stock of him. The burned scar in the center of his forehead, and his tremendously long earlobes proclaimed him a member of the local tribe; but when I greeted him in Chigogo, the language of Central Tanganyika,* he took not the slightest notice.

"*Mbukwa*," I repeated. "Good day."

Like Tar Baby, he said nothing.

"*Mbukwa*," I repeated again, raising my voice.

"*Twi*," said Daudi, "not a word. Try him in Swahili, Bwana."

"*Jambo*," I said. "Jambo! *Jambo!*"

Daudi smiled. Then I tried a couple of other languages.

"*Kamweni*" (the greeting of the Wahehe, the neighboring tribe).

Again no reply.

"*Mwangaluka*," I greeted, using the language of the people of the Mountains of the Moon.

This seemed to produce results at last. He looked up, but there was no light of comprehension in his eyes. He slouched

---

*In 1964, Tanganyika became Tanzania.

off, sat down on a three-legged stool, and put his head in his hands, and groaned.

I had an idea; and taking a piece of paper, I wrote, "Why are you so sad?"

I handed it to him and was not reassured when he held it upside down and looked at it glumly. I felt we'd reached a deadlock. I could think of nothing more to be done. I racked my brains for some new line of attack, when the miserable figure suddenly threw the paper to the ground and said firmly, "I can't read and I can't hear. I'm just worthless."

He rose wearily, but I grasped his shoulder and pushed him back. Daudi brought the ear examination tray; and, pulling my stethoscope from my pocket, I put the ear part into his ears, and yelled down the chest piece, "Can you hear now?"

A slow smile spread over his black face. *"Yoh,* Bwana, that's better. *Heee,* I can hear. Then, surely, I'm not bewitched." Then he seemed struck by an idea. "Bwana," he cried excitedly, "I'll give you a cow for this thing."

He waved the stethoscope hopefully in the air and then caressed its rubber tubes. I tried to make him grasp that I could make his hearing better by medical means; but in his enthusiasm, he seemed to think that I was holding out for a higher price; so he proceeded to bargain, "Bwana, I'll pay a cow and a goat—a fat one."

I shook my head and opened a little black box that the dresser (male nurse or orderly) who had just reached us, panting, handed to me. Adjusting a trumpet-shaped instrument, fitted with a minute electric bulb that gave a clear view into any ear, I motioned my deaf friend to keep still; but he was suspicious. I put the stethoscope back into place, and bellowed, "I'm going to look into your ears. Look in front, and keep your head still."

The answer was a beaming smile and the reply, *"Yeh! Bwana, I can hear a noise like bees swarming."*

Daudi chuckled. In desperation, I grasped our patient by the earlobe, and peered in. The whole ear was blocked with tar-like wax, and I saw some remnants of grass.

"Muganga, the witch doctor," remarked Daudi. The other ear was even worse and had obviously been prodded with a thorn.

"How long have you been deaf?" I yelled.

"No, Bwana," said the patient.

Daudi yelled at the top of his voice, repeating the question.

"Oh," said the patient, raising his eyebrows.

We laughed. It was hopeless.

"Syringe out those ears, Daudi, and then we'll have some fun."

I went back to my work; and about an hour later, I came back to find Daudi hard at it, syringing. There was a grim line about his mouth, and the patient had a pathetic look in his eye.

"What's up, Daudi? Things not so good?"

"Kah," said Daudi, "Bwana, here am I just squirting the fiftieth syringe into his ears, and not a bit of wax. *Kah!"*

"Try the other ear, Daudi."

I saw the grinning face of a junior dresser hugely enjoying the joke, so I called out to him; and the last I saw was Daudi sitting in the shade, while his junior set to work, filling and emptying the syringe into the ear of the patient. An hour later, I returned to find a weary dresser and a depressed patient. I tested the latter with the stethoscope.

"Can you hear?"

"Yes, Bwana."

"I'm going to put medicine in your ears to soften the wax that's there."

He nodded his head so enthusiastically that the stethoscope came out. Undaunted, he shook my hand vigorously and said I was his father and mother.

I went into the dispensary and wrote a prescription; Samson read it over, took up measures, and, deftly mixing the contents of sundry bottles, soon had the stuff dispensed. He neatly wrote a label, stuck it on, and presented me with the bottle and an eardropper. Our patient watched everything with wide eyes; and as I filled the dropper, he opened his mouth. Once again the stethoscope came into use, and soon the drops were in his ears. I explained that tomorrow, when the wax had been softened a bit, we would syringe again; and then we could hope for results.

I called the African staff together and, using this case as an example, set them to work to demonstrate ear treatment. Everyone sat watching keenly, while James prepared an ear tray. He set out three bowls, one with sterile water, one with peroxide, and one with cotton wool. There was also the syringe and a kidney dish.

"Bwana," said the dresser. "This dish has warm water in it and bicarbonate of soda. This is just for ordinary syringing."

"Why is the water warm?" I asked, hurling the question

at a junior nurse. She gaped, shook her head, and no one seemed to know; so with cold water her ears were syringed. After the third treatment, she said, *Yoh!* I feel giddy," then staggered and fell.

It was a demonstration no one ever forgot.

"Why use a kidney-shaped dish?" was the next question. James' answer was eloquent. He held a round bowl to the neck of the dresser and then the kidney-shaped one.

"See," he cried. "It saves the water from being spilled down the patient's neck."

The next morning, I took up my otoscope and peered into the patient's ear again. The wax looked brownish and soft. Daudi appeared with his kerosene can half full of hot water, his syringe, a kidney bowl, and some cotton-wool swabs. He led the deaf man over to the tomato garden, sat him down on a stool, and loaded up. A crowd of small boys stood around to watch. With a twinkle in his eye, Daudi squirted a syringeful into their faces. They gasped and fled. The deaf man laughed heartily, and said in a megaphone-like voice, *"Yoh,* behold, that medicine moves things."

Still smiling, Daudi grasped the man's ear, put the nozzle in position, and squirted. The first syringeful was uneventful, but the second one was colored faintly brown.

"It's coming, Bwana," said Daudi; and come it did, halfway through the third round.

With a yell, the deaf man pulled his ear from Daudi's grasp, knocked stool and bowl flying, and proceeded to execute a triumphant dance among the tomato plants, to the intense worry of James, who prodded him with a broom, and at the top of his voice shouted, *"Kah,* be careful of my garden!"

"Yoh," said the dancer, with a grin that was at once wide and broad. "Don't bother to raise your voice for me now. Was I not rejoicing because once again I can hear?"

"Sit down again," ordered Daudi. "You've got *two* ears to be fixed up. Let me finish the work."

He carefully picked up a black mass that had come from the ear and showed me a gum, which apparently was the witch doctor's treatment. Shrugging his shoulders, the dresser picked up the syringe again; and in a few minutes, the whole thing was over.

Daudi peered into the ear, and said, "Clear, I can see the drum." In his hand were the wax plugs.

Now, Daudi believed in the value of attack. He held the wax under the nose of our latest triumph. "There, don't you ever tell me you can't understand what sin is. Here is a picture of it, and it tells its own story."·

The poor fellow gasped. *"Yoh,"* he said. "That only stopped me from hearing your words."

"Swanu," said Daudi. "Right, and sin stops you from hearing and understanding God. Now that your ears work, it is your responsibility to reply when people talk to you. Behold, now you must hear the Word of God, when He says, 'The wages of sin is death, but the gift of God is eternal life through   Jesus Christ.' "

"Yoh," said the man, "it is hard to understand."

"Well," said Daudi, "stay close, and you will hear more. Behold, if you go to your home, more wax will come; and soon you will be deaf again. Stay near, and we can remove the wax each time it appears."

"Behold," said James, "is that not like sin? If you go far from the Lord Jesus, soon you lose the hearing of your soul. But stay close to where He can help you. Then all is well."

"Behold, I will stay," said the once deaf man.

"*Swanu*, good," said Daudi, "for you have a new responsibility. Did not Jesus say, 'he that hath ears to hear, let him hear'?"

"*Eeeeee*," said the man. "You have taken the blockage from my ears and opened for my mind new thoughts."

"Yes, that's what we're here for," said Daudi.

2

FATHER AND SON

In the shade of the huge trunk of a baobab tree that grew not far from our hospital, sat an old man, dressed in a very dirty square yard of black cloth, with red mud in his hair. He took no notice of me as I came up. He seemed altogether too busy with the shaft of an arrow which he held firmly in his left hand and gripped at the other end with two very agile big toes. He smoothed it in a couple of places with a razor-sharp handmade ax. He then let out a grunt of approval and fitted a barb, which I suspected had once been a portion of the iron highway of the Tanganyika railway system. Very dexterously, he bound this barb into position with some sisal fiber and then dipped it into a small clay pot containing a filthy-looking black concoction. I turned to Kefa, the dresser, who had come up beside me. "What's the stuff he's putting on the arrow?"

Said the African, "Bwana, *sumu* [poison]. *Heh,* and it's very deadly."

There was something very fascinating in watching the nimble fingers of that old man carrying out the craft which had been practiced by his tribe for centuries; and somehow, to me, that black concoction inside the earthenware pot seemed to bring up a string of pictures of witch doctors; of murder in the night due to poison, which was called witchcraft; of all manner of devilry, which lay just under the surface of life in Central Tanganyika.

Kefa touched me on the shoulder. "Bwana," he whispered, "do you know who this old man is?"

"No," I said, as we walked off toward the hospital. "I don't exactly. I've seen him around the village, and I gave him a lift once in the car; but I've never seen him actually at the hospital. He doesn't seem to like our medicine. Who is he, anyhow?"

Kefa laughed. "Bwana, come with me, and I'll show you his son."

"All right then. Is his son an expert with arrows?"

"Bwana, I'm not sure; but he uses other things to stab people with."

"Hongo! That sounds dangerous. Is he a patient in the hospital, or what?"

"Bwana, come and see." Kefa smiled broadly, as he led me through the gateway, past the men's ward and the dispensary. Then he stopped outside a window and pointed inside with his stick. There I saw an African in his late twenties. He was looking down a microscope and his fingers moved skillfully over the adjustments.

"There, Bwana," said Kefa. "There is the son of the poisoned-arrow expert."

For a moment I was speechless. It was Daudi, my head dispenser.

It seemed so incongruous. The father an expert in Stone Age craft, the son an expert in detecting tropical disease and in the use of a highly specialized scientific instrument. I had spoken to the old man in the Central African dialect, and here was the son, a most capable linguist.

Suddenly the dispenser looked up from the eyepiece of his microscope and said in excellent English, "You'll pardon me, Bwana, but would you mind looking at this slide? I cannot convince myself that it is benign tertian malaria. I'd like your opinion on it, if you'll be so good."

I examined the slide, and for a few minutes we were engaged in a very technical conversation. As Daudi fitted another slide into the stage of the microscope, I asked, "Do you know I've been talking to your father outside?"

"*Kumbe*," said the African. "Bwana, I suppose he was making arrows. Behold, is he not an expert at that? It's his way of making money."

"*Hongo*, might it not well have been that you would have followed on in your father's craft and made arrows?"

Daudi nodded his head slowly.

"Well," I continued, "why did you leave your way of living and take on your present job in the hospital with us?"

"It all started when I was a small boy, Bwana. I went to a mission school—a little place with a few gasoline drums for desks and benches made of hardened mud. There I learned to read. The only book we had was the New Testament; so of course I heard the story of Jesus. When I heard it, I decided I would go His way and I would be a member of His tribe; so I did this, and I took His Book as my guide. Behold, as I read more, I understood the mistakes that people had made by not following God and not living His way. I determined not to follow their paths."

"But your father, Daudi. Does he take any interest in these things?"

"No, Bwana, he says his way is good enough for him. You see, Bwana, he puts more trust in the charm he wears around his neck than in the quinine which I would give him for his malaria. When he shivers and perspires and aches all over, he thinks it is witchcraft. I know differently. Does not the microscope make it clear to me? *Heh,* Bwana, in just the same way, my reading of the Bible helps me to understand about sin and its penalty, and about the Saviour and the cure He came to bring and died to make available."

A week later, coming to the hospital, I found Daudi's father standing under the same baobab tree. This time he had no arrows or poison to put on them, and he greeted me in a strange, husky voice. *"Heh,* Bwana," he said, "I am in great trouble—trouble which I fear will cause me to walk the path to my ancestors. Behold, I cannot eat food. I can barely talk. Today, Bwana, I cannot swallow water. Behold, I will die."

"Hongo, perhaps I have medicine which will help."

"Kah, Bwana, have you?"

I took him with me into the outpatients' room and put on a head mirror. Although for a moment he was a bit scared of it, I managed to get him to open his mouth wide. The mirror caught the brightness of the early morning sun and reflected the light down his throat. He had a huge swelling.

As I completed my examination, Daudi came through the door. *"Kah,* Bwana," said he, speaking in Chigogo, "behold my father."

"Truly, Daudi. He has much trouble with his throat, but it is not a trouble that we cannot deal with. Behold, he has a great *ipu* [an abscess]."

"*Kumbe*," said the old man harshly, "it is more than that, Bwana; there are those that wish me evil at this time, and someone has cast a spell."

"My father," said Daudi, "have you not consulted Muganga, the witch doctor? Has he not given you medicine, and yet you are no better?"

"*Hey, hey*," nodded the old man, putting his hand to his throat; it hurt him acutely to speak.

"Well," said my friend the dispenser, "let the Bwana use his medicine."

"*Kah*," said the old man, "since I am going to die, what harm can it do me?"

Daudi's eyes twinkled. For just such cases as these, I had been sent some special anesthetic that is injected into a vein. The patient is asleep in a matter of seconds. The doctor has at least ten minutes to do the small operation required.

Everything was made ready, but within view of Daudi's father. The injection was given into his arm. For a moment I talked to him.

"Bwana," he said, "the ways of the Europeans are very strange ways. Behold, I do not think they a-a-r-r—" His voice just faded away; he was unconscious. It is a very rapidly acting drug. Quickly Daudi and I worked in our jungle operating room. In a few moments, the abscess was no more. Everything was put away by the time the old man opened his eyes again and said, "*Keh—ooh*, behold I can speak. Ooh, I have thirst." He was given a drink. Then he looked across at me. "Bwana," he said, "that's medicine. Behold there was never anything in the country of Ugogo like that!"

I said nothing.

"My *ipu* has gone." Then in a strange voice, "Behold, this is witchcraft!"

"This, my father," said Daudi, "is not witchcraft but wisdom. Behold, pain disappears in this place when you follow the Bwana's words, as sin is blotted out when you follow the words and ways of Jesus."

The old man shook his head. "Behold, I am too old to understand these things. I must follow in the ways of the tribe."

To my knowledge, on no occasion did he ever change his point of view.

One day I discussed it all with Daudi.

"It's very hard to touch my father, Bwana. Behold, is he not like concrete? He is set hard, and his ways are difficult ways."

"Truly, Daudi, concrete is hard; yet if you hit at it with a hammer, each blow may not seem to crack it; but the time will come when a small crack appears and then a larger one, and then the concrete is broken. Behold, the ways of our hospitals are like that, and the ways of our teachings are like that also. We help people, we take their pain away, we give them relief, we tell them the message, and one day it sinks in."

Daudi nodded slowly.

As I looked at father and son, I thought of the tremendous changes that were coming to Africa—the old man, trusting in a charm for his health and his future, in a poisoned arrow and a primitive hoe for his food; and then his son, with a reasoned faith in a living God, with a valuable contribution to make to the knowledge and welfare of his own people.

The main difference between them was that the old man had turned his back on God; but the son had heard the good news of new life and was actively following the Son of God, whose own statement was, "I am come that they might have life, and that they might have it more abundantly."

3

HANDFUL OF SEED

"Samson," I said, "I want you to write to the chief of the village called Mhundulu."

"*Ah-hah,* Bwana," said the African, "what do you want him to do for you?"

"I am going over there, because there are many women in that village who do not visit our hospital. Behold, their babies are very sick—many of them die—and I would speak with the women. I would examine their children and bring them medicines. I would show them the ways of the hospital here and get them to come."

"*Koh,* Bwana," said Samson, this will be no easy thing. This village is a place where the witch doctor is very strong."

"*Yoh,*" said Daudi, looking up from his microscope, "but behold the chief of that village had a very bad toothache, and did not the Bwana help him very much with his forceps?"

"*Heeh,*" said Samson, "well, I'll write the letter, Bwana."

"Before you do, come away from that microscope, Daudi, and let's ask God to help us in contacting this village."

We knelt around a gasoline can on the floor, and each

prayed that God would help us to bring the message of better things to the folk of that particular village in the jungle; and that as they found the better things for health, they would also see that the ways of God were very important to their lives.

Two hours later, I saw an African bearing my letter in a cleft stick, walking out through the hospital gate, underneath the row of baobab trees, over the dry riverbed, and through the cornfields on his way to the jungle village. where I had reason to believe that seven out of every ten children died before they even had their first birthday.

The next day a letter came back. The chief would have great joy if the Bwana would visit his village. He would make ready for him a room in his own house. He would see that the women came; and to prove his very good will toward me, he sent me a gourd full of eggs. There proved to be thirty-four of them, of which twenty-two were decidedly discolored.

I found I could drive along pathways for some ten miles of the journey. This I did in the very early morning and walked the additional seven miles in the cool of the day. For fully three miles, we walked through cornfields along one of the most fertile stretches of the country. The corn was six feet high; the pathway wound tortuously through the middle of it. Everybody seemed busy about scaring away the small birds which came down in flocks to take the ripening millet seeds. Men stood ready with their bows and arrows to take potshots at the monkeys that came scampering out of the jungle, pulling whole ears of corn and rushing back to the shelter of the trees. Old men and women sat on raised platforms and pulled long ropes stretched across the crops with pieces of paper, old cans—anything—tied onto them. The movement and the clatter kept the birds away.

"Kah," said Sechelela who was with me. "very many people will not come for medicine today. They will say, 'Should we leave our crops to be eaten by the birds? Is it not better to have more sickness than to die of great famine?' "

When we arrived at the village, there were no less than twenty-seven women and children waiting to see us, and also the chief, dressed in a newly-ironed *kanzu* [a long, flowing garment] that completely covered a whole lot of things underneath, which I felt sure weren't as clean as the flowing white garment, which looked conspicuously like a nightshirt.

"Bwana," said he, "you are very welcome to visit my village. Behold, I have made many preparations for you. There is a special place for you to *pima* [examine] those who have sicknesses."

I ducked my head to enter a room of his mud-and-wattle house. It was just tall enough to stand up in. There was an overpowering smell from the floor, which was made from a mixture of cow manure and mud, trodden till it was hard. It had been washed over for our benefit, and small pools of highly pungent water remained. I moved across into the lighter portion of this room, and a hen and three chicks scurried out of my way. I seated myself on a three-legged stool that the chief had provided, and carefully brushed off a cockroach which fell from the roof. Soon we were ready to start. Sechelela had an African-made bed brought in, on which we would do the examinations; but our patients weren't very happy about it.

"*Yoh*," said one, "send him out; we will not tell him the secrets of our sickness."

"*Heh*," said Sechelela, "is not he the doctor? Does he not know everything?"

This was a little too much for me, and I had to turn my laughter into a rather decorous cough.

Before long, case after case was duly examined and medicine given. Every one of them seemed to have malaria. Scores of them showed tropical diseases of all sorts, and I heard the pathetic story of how child after child had died quite unnecessarily; flies just swarmed around the place and crawled unresisted into the eyes of the children and babies. Some were given injections; some were given medicine which would make all the difference.

When I came out of the close, stuffy atmosphere of that African house into the open air, I found a vast collection of people who had come to greet me and to taste my medicine.

"What are you suffering from?" I said. "What are your troubles?"

"*Kah*," they replied. "We have none, but we've come to taste your medicine."

Sechelela tapped me on the shoulder. "Bwana," she said, "you must give them medicine. There will be great grief if they do not get any. Behold, we have a great bottle of Epsom salts here. Let us mix that up and give it to them."

And so every one of at least one hundred fifty folk who had come along, solemnly drank a strong dose of Epsom salts, smacked their lips, and said, "*Yoh*, what medicine!"

As they all stood there listening, old Sechelela told them
the story that Jesus had told of the sower and seed. They all
nodded their heads. Was not this the time when much
sowing had gone on?

"Behold," she said, "do we not know how some of the
seed does not come up, and how in other places the weeds
grow up and choke the young corn? Behold, do not the birds
take other seeds?"

"Heh-heh," the Africans said, nodding. "Does this not
happen?"

"But," said Sechelela, "there is the good, prepared
ground; into this, the seed falls and grows, and there is a big
crop."

"Heh-heh," said the people. "These are words we
understand."

"Koh, Bwana," said the chief, "I perceive that this story
is a riddle. There is a meaning behind it. Tell us, what is the
meaning?"

"Behold," I said, "the story of the sower was told by
Jesus, the Son of God; and just as you have asked the
answer, so did those who followed Him. Remember, the
Words of God are the seed. Jesus says of them, 'When a
man hears the words concerning the kingdom of God but
does not understand them, then Shaitan comes and takes
away what has been sown in his heart.' This is like the
case that Sechelela told you of; when the seed falls on the
hard trodden path, nothing grows there. But then he who
receives the seed on stony ground is the man who hears the
Word and at the beginning is filled with happiness and
enthusiasm, but he has small wish to obey God's words; the

earth is too shallow; he strikes no roots. When he finds the way hard, he turns his back on the ways of God.

"He who receives the seed among the weeds is the man who hears the Word, but all the worries of his everyday living and his desire for much money, *heh,* this stifles the Word and it doesn't grow. But the one who hears the Word and receives the seed, as it were, on good ground, is the man who hears and understands; and for such people there is a harvest."

"Hoh," said the chief, "Bwana, these are hard words to understand."

"Truly, great one, read the words of God in this Book." I gave him one. Then I pointed to my box with all the medicines and injections and all the rest of the things.

"Behold," I continued, "those medicines will help your body to be well; but in this Book is the answer to every problem that could be met by anyone in his life."

"Kumbe," said the chief. "Behold, we would need a teacher to read the words to us and teach us to understand them."

From behind the crowd of people standing there, a sixteen-year-old boy came forward.

"Great one," he said, "behold, when I was in the mission hospital when I had *muhunga* [the great fever], behold, I was weak; and when I grew strong, I learned to read the Word. Behold, I will read for you the words of the Book that the Bwana has given to you."

We bade them all farewell,; and as we walked through the corn, Sechelela said, "Bwana, that boy who spoke, behold he is one who heard the Word. Behold, there is a harvest in his heart."

"*Eh-heh,*" I replied, "and the sowing will go on in this village."

4

DYNAMITE

I crouched on the shady side of my car, on the Cape to Cairo road. An Indian's truck rolled by, driven by an Arab. It was grossly overloaded with packages of all sorts, surmounted by a singing group of Africans, who yelled a greeting at me. I waved back, as I put a patch on the offending inner tube. Then, with an old pair of dental forceps, I dragged a two-and-a-half inch thorn from the tire. It was just one of the hold ups that a jungle doctor had to expect. Carefully I put the tube back, replaced the valve, and proceeded to jump on the wheel in the way required to get the cover back into position.

With a sigh of relief, I pumped up the tire and put the wheel back on the car. Then, as I let down the jack, to my intense chagrin, I found that the front tire was flat also! I resignedly had started to put the jack into position under the front wheel, when I heard the rattle of a car. Half a minute later, with a grinding of brakes, a public works department truck pulled up.

"Hello, doctor," the cheery official said, laughing. It was his Herculean task to keep this vital East African highway in repair. "What's cooking?"

I wiped the sweat from my brow with a dusty hand. "Punctures, George," I groaned, "punctures."

He laughed again, and turning to the African aide beside him, said in Swahili, "Would you fix up the Bwana's puncture at once?" and to me he said, "Come and have a cuppa."

Gratefully, I surrendered my tools to the young African, and soon was telling my friend of my various troubles.

"It's this way, George. Our job's booming. The more success we have, the more patients we get; and the more patients we get, the more success we have. And so on, like Rudyard Kipling's fleas, 'ad infinitum.'"

George laughed and poured me out another cup. "And so what are you doing about it?"

"Well, I'm building a new maternity ward, taking the old veranda that we used to sun the babies on, building it in; and I reckon I can do the whole job for a hundred shillings. But it means quarrying stone. Now I've got three fellows with hammers and crowbars and wedges, but they don't make much headway on the granite that we have out near Mvumi. Now, give me the benefit of your expert knowledge. What do you suggest?"

"Ten shillings," said George, "for that."

"Wrong," I countered, "that's the cost of saving a life. The consultation fee at Mvumi is a halfpenny, or a bundle of sticks, or a handful of grain, or an egg."

My companion whistled and pulled two five-shilling notes from his pocket. "I didn't realize you could do things as cheaply as that; anyway, here's a life."

I gripped his hand. Little did he realize how painfully low were our finances. In a week I would pay the wages, and there was not nearly enough money to cover them.

"Bwana," reported the aide, "puncture's mended."

"Well, doc," said my friend, "why not dynamite tha rock? I'll come out and do it for you on Saturday afternoon."

"Great," I replied. "Thanks so much."

I waved good-bye, as his car disappeared in a cloud o dust. After some complicated jiggling with sundry string and wires, and with a little judicious pushing, I also went or my way.

Later that afternoon, I went to our quarry. There were three men working there, all of them lepers. In each case the disease was burned out. They had no trace of infection, but the ravages of the disease were painfully visible in the lack of toe joints and finger joints. Their faces were scarred by the activities of this all too common complaint. They smiled up at me.

"Yoh! Bwana, this is work. These stones are hard and will not crack. It is time wasted. Behold, we only have this amount."

They pointed to a heap. It certainly was not enough to keep the masons going on our new project. There was one big mass of stone, and pointing to it, I asked, "What about that bit?"

They shook their heads. "No, Bwana, it is too hard."

I nodded. "Do you remember in the Bible it says that Jesus is the stone which the builders rejected? And behold, He became the chief stone in the whole building."

"Truly," said one of the men. "if Jesus had not come, what would life be for such as we? We would have nothing to look forward to in this life." He held up his mutilated hands.

'But Bwana, there are so many who do not understand these things."

"Right," I replied. "Let's preach a parable to them. Go around the village and say that there is a stone that the Bwana says he will break in two, and that he will use it as the main stone in the building. And tell them that for days you have tried to crack it and can do nothing. Just do that, and we will teach them a lesson they will never forget."

Then I showed them how to drill holes in this mass of granite. One of them, who was an expert blacksmith, had a charcoal fire, which he blew with an ingenious bellows which he had made from fire-baked clay and a goatskin. On an old piece of railway track which he used as an anvil, he sharpened drills and crowbars. Soon the quite sizeable holes were drilled in the granite. Apparently my quarrymen had done their job well, for people came to look at the stone and laughed.

"Behold, no one could crack that stone. It is not possible; it is too big."

"Yoh," said one of the quarrymen, "behold, the hearts of many people are as stone; but the Bwana tells us of a God who has power to crack hearts of stone."

"Yoh!" sneered one old man named Mugoli, who prided himself on his disbelief. "If the Bwana can crack that stone, then perhaps I would listen to this story of the power that cracks hearts." There were smiles from some of his friends.

I had come up just in time to hear this. "Right," I said, "you be here on Saturday. I will have that stone cracked into many pieces, with a crack that will make you run for your life."

"Heee," they laughed, "this is impossible."

"Hongo," I said, "on Saturday then."

When the great day arrived, there was quite a crowd to watch proceedings. My good friend turned up, armed with dynamite, fuses, and all sorts of paraphernalia. He looked at the bored holes, and held out the dynamite for the inspection of the crowd.

"Yoh," said the skeptical man, "behold, it looks like a sausage. *Heee*, what good can that do? I am not frightened of that."

"Listen," I said, "there is danger. If you do not run when the Bwana here lights this piece of string that fizzes, then behold, you may be badly hurt."

Everybody was most impressed, except Mugoli, who said, *"I* have no fear; it can't hurt *me."*

I translated this for my public works companion. He smiled. "I will set off a small charge first, and we will see what he does then."

Emboldened by his seeming success, Mugoli proceeded to deliver an oration. "I do not worship the God of the Europeans. My ancestors are good enough for me."

"But," said Daudi, "Jesus Christ, God's Son, was not a European, nor yet an African, but He was the link between them."

"Yoh," laughed Mugoli, "I do not believe in Him. I do not believe in the words of His Book. I will not believe anything I cannot understand."

I held up one of the greasy packets of dynamite.

"Listen, great talker. Can you understand this? This stuff is medicine of great power that will split that rock."

The African, now thoroughly pleased with the impression he was making, retorted, *"Yoh,* it could not."

My friend tamped down the charge, fixed the fuse, and said, "Run, all of you. Hide behind rocks or in holes; for, after I light this, soon there will be a loud *bang;* and the rock will be torn by the strength of this medicine."

There was a great scurry, and even Mugoli moved back somewhat. He leaned against the trunk of a great baobab tree. I moved to a safe distance and crouched behind a rock and smiled, as I saw scores of Africans crouching apprehensively, waiting to see what would happen. With a yell to "Look out!" my friend touched off the fuse and ran to crouch down beside me. There was a dead silence, and in it Mugoli moved forward from his vantage point.

"Behold," he said, "nothing happened. It was a lie. Who would believe the words of the Bwana? Behold, he is not one—"

At that moment, the dynamite exploded with a roar. Bits of stone were showered down, one of them cruising perilously close to the doubter. With a yell that rivaled the explosion, he took to his heels, followed by the derisive laughter of the assembled Africans. But when they saw us approach the rock, which was neatly split in two, they gathered confidence and came around.

"There," said my friend, "that will show you that we do not talk lies, but the truth."

The old African clergyman who had been quietly watching proceedings, held up his hands, "Tomorrow I want you to come with the doubting one to the church; and behold, I will tell you the story of today."

Next morning, he preached with his New Testament in one hand and a stick of dynamite in the other. It certainly was an effective talk. "I am not ashamed of the gospel, the good news of Jesus Christ, for it is the power of God unto salvation. Through this power, sin is conquered and kept conquered; and a way is made open to us to have life forever, as well as to have the help of God with us here."

In the backseat, sitting very quietly, was Mugoli, with all the bounce taken out of him. He turned up at the hospital as the new piles of stone were brought up and the masons completed a job that was vitally important for the expansion of our work. Day after day he watched, as the dynamite-split stone was built in. Then one day I found him talking to one of the leper quarrymen.

"Behold," said one of our workmen, "it says in God's Book that many people will not believe in Jesus because He does not offer an easy life to those who follow Him. He offers solid toil, and no laziness, and no easy road."

He held up his scarred and gnarled hands, "But for leprosy, I would never have understood about God, nor bothered to think about Him."

Mugoli shook his head. "No, I want to follow my own way," he said, and strode away from the hospital.

The quarryman took up his crowbar again, and after prying out a great square of granite, turned to me, and said, "Bwana, how true are Jesus' words, that the road to death and destruction is broad, easy, and kind to the feet."

I nodded. "Especially when it is softened by much wealth."

5

CHIEF'S EYE

It was one of those burning hot days, when heat shimmered over the plains. The baobab tree stood out against the glare, and it was an effort even to breathe. As usual, quite a fair proportion of the tropical night had been spent in our maternity ward, and I was tired and depressed, and the fear that our job wasn't accomplishing all that it should, came upon me as I sweltered in my mud brick office.

"Hodi," came a voice, and Daudi appeared.

"Bwana." he said, "we have a visitor, Mwaluko, the chief from Ng'hati, a rich man, with many cows."

"Hongo, Daudi. I remember him. We did his cataract last June."

"Yes, Bwana, and he is back today, and he wants to tell you what it means to him. I warn you, Bwana, he is a man of many words!"

"Well, bring him in, Daudi, and I will listen to what he has to say. I feel much more like words than works!"

A moment later I was solemnly shaking hands with an old man, and asking after his health, his gardens, his home, his cattle, and his wives. There were seven of the latter, and thereby hangs this tale.

At long last, he sat down on a three-legged stool, and in a deep voice started his story.

35

"Behold, Bwana, I am a great chief, with great herds, a big house, and my seven wives. I am a chief who rides on a donkey. Before I came to the hospital I was *mushenzi*[a heathen]. I knew not God. Six of my wives were like me, but one was not; she was called Mwamvula."

"*Kumbe,* and what was she?"

"She, Bwana, was a Christian. Some time before, the Christians had built a little church of mud and wickerwork in the next village. Mwamvula went each Sunday to hear the words of God, but all my other wives laughed at her.

"It was about this time, Bwana, that *mabulibuli* [mists] began to appear before my eyes. I rubbed them, but the mist remained. The days passed, and it grew thicker and thicker, until my sight grew dimmer and dimmer; and I could no longer see. I couldn't see my wives, or my cows, or my house.

"So I said to myself, 'I must go to the witch doctor. Perhaps he will be able to give me something to bring back my sight.' Five of my *wawaha* [counselors] and two of my wives led me to the witch doctor's house and helped me off my white donkey, and I made a *shauri* with the witch doctor. But *hongo!* He had seen me coming a long way off, and he said in his heart, 'Here comes the chief; he seeks medicine. He is a rich man, so I will be able to get a very big gift for my medicine.' To me he said, 'Yes, I can make your eyes better, but it is a difficult medicine. You will see again if you give me that big bull of yours. Then I will dig you medicines, cook them and you shall drink this, and in a few days, light will return to your eyes.'

" 'I will certainly give you the bull,' I replied; and I sent a messenger to Ndalu, my herdsman, telling him to send me the biggest bull immediately, so that I might receive my sight. When the bull was brought, the witch doctor examined it carefully, went away into the jungle, and came back with a basket containing leaves and roots. He put them into a big clay pot with honey and the liver of a white cock, and cooked them for an hour.

" 'Your medicine is ready,' he said, and he took the pot, which contained a green, slimy mess, and made me drink it all. Ugh, I was sick! Behold, my inside turned this way and that way for days. But I thought it was worth it, if I could see. My wives rose up to help me, for the pain was very great. 'What does it matter,' I said, 'if only I receive light again?'

"But the days passed, and no light came. So I knew that I had been deceived by the witch doctor; he had lied to me. I was in great distress for many days, then one of the old men came to me and said, 'My father, there is a medicine man who lives over at Ihogolo; men say he has much wisdom. Perhaps he will help your blindness.'

" 'Kah,' I replied, 'I shall go anywhere, if I can but see again.' So I mounted my donkey and traveled many miles through lion country. Muganga, the medicine man, said, 'Give me that spear and those shoes that you are wearing, and I will make your eyes better.' "

The old man stretched out his hands toward me. "Behold, Bwana, I had a very beautiful, long, sharp, shiny spear. It had belonged to my father and was very precious to me. And my shoes were the same as the white man's; I had bought them for much money in the big town. But what are shoes and spears in comparison with eyesight? So I told the medicine man to work his cure.

"Then he chewed something up in his mouth and spat it into my eyes. Ugh, it burned! For days I groaned in my house. Then I realized that I had been deceived once more.

"Again my counselors persuaded me to go to another witch doctor. He said, 'Give me the white donkey on which you ride, and I will heal your eyes, so that you will see again.' So I gave him my beautiful donkey, and he took some charms and hung them around my neck and my wrists, and said, 'These charms have great power in them. Wear them, and in a few days your sight will be restored.' "

He handed me some dirty pieces of cowhide. As I examined them, he spat forcibly and disgustedly through the doorway.

"*Kah*. Bwana, I was deceived for the third time. Then great was my sorrow, because not only were my eyes no better, but I had lost my bull, my donkey, my spear, and my shoes."

"Oh chief," I sympathized, "great was your sorrow indeed. But why did you come to our hospital?"

"It was this way, Bwana. One Sunday Mwamvula came home from church and said, 'Oh chief, the Christians at the church where I go to worship God tell me that at Mvumi is a hospital of the people of God. They cure many diseases, and even blind men have gone there and found their eyesight again.'

"So I called my counselors together yet again, and said, 'Hear the words of my wife. Let us go to Mvumi.' So the next day we started on the safari. One of my counselors went in front, holding one end of a long stick. I followed, holding the other end. *Yoh,* it was a long journey. How I longed for my strong leather shoes and for my white donkey! Thorns pierced my feet, and my legs grew very tired.

"At last we arrived, and I rested in a comfortable bed, such as I had never slept in before. Three times each day came an African male nurse and rubbed *mafuta* [ointment] around my eyes, and poured blue medicine into them.

"But one day they cut my eyelashes short with scissors, and said, 'Tomorrow, the Bwana will cut your eyes, and then you will be able to see.'

" 'Yoh,' I said, 'my misery is great. Will not the pain be much? Oh, my troubles are more than I can bear! I have suffered many things of many witch doctors, and still I cannot see.'

" 'You need not be afraid,' said James, 'for the Bwana will put medicine in your eyes before he cuts it, medicine that takes away pain. But you must be good when he cuts your eye. You must remain perfectly still. You must look at the top of your head, or down at your feet exactly when the Bwana says. If you don't, or if you shake with fear, you will ruin the Bwana's work.'

" 'I will do as you say,' I promised. 'Anything, if the Bwana makes my eyes better.' Then he prayed, and asked God to help me, and you also, Bwana; and when he had finished, I said 'Amen.'

"Next day I walked to the operating room. They laid me on a table. They put the painkilling drug into my eyes. My face was covered. Cold things kept my eyes open. Again they prayed, and I lifted up my heart to God, and asked that I might see. And when they had finished praying, I said 'Amen' again, very loudly.

"You said, 'Look up,' Bwana. I looked up. You said 'Look down,' and I looked down. You said, 'Quietly gently,' and then I heard you sigh; and my joy was very great; for behold, there was light! I could see people moving Then I saw your face, and you said, 'What was that?' 'A finger,' I replied. 'And that?' 'Three fingers,' I said joyfully.

"All the hospital helpers standing around laughed with joy. But you said, 'Now keep still, don't get excited, you eyes must be bandaged.' How quietly I lay! *Yoh*, the bed was hard! My joints stuck through my skin! But it was worth it all. And each day James came and talked to me about God.

"When the bandages came off, I said, 'Now I know that only the people of God speak the truth. Three times have I been deceived by bad men and gave of my riches without getting better. But I came here to the hospital, and they restored my sight. Yes, I know these words which I have heard about God and about Jesus are true. I know, Bwana, that Jesus is my Saviour, and that I have eternal life through Him' Behold, now I go to church with Mwamvula. My other wives also go. They have ceased to laugh at her. For was it not through her word that I am now able to see?'"

I watched the old man walk around the ward to greet the other patients. I had forgotten the time—the heat seemed merely comfortable; I put my topee on and went on with the job, confident that never had a job been more worthwhile, or ten shillings better spent than in dealing with the old chieftain, Mwaluko.

6

MENDING BONES AND LIVES

Kefa, one of our dressers, had been giving us trouble. He was pigheaded and stubborn and difficult, and his work was slovenly; so I called him into my office.

"Are you not feeling well these days?"

"Oh, I'm all right, Bwana," he said ungraciously.

"Has your wife lost her skill in cooking?"

"No, Bwana."

"Oh, I see, it's like that, is it? Well, listen, there was a man who had a tooth, and at the bottom of this tooth there was a germ. That germ married, lived happily, and had a very large family; and before long, his tribe was a large and prosperous one, so prosperous that the man's tooth ached and ached, as the germ village increased in size. Behold, he lost interest in his work; he beat his children; he thrashed his wife, until one day he came to us, and we removed the tooth and destroyed the village of germs. Then, behold, that man's smile returned; he loved his wife and his children; his garden was the best in the village."

"*Yoh!*" said Kefa. "Bwana, what are you talking about?"

"You—there's something wrong."

"There's nothing wrong," said Kefa. "I do not beat my wife."

"No," I replied, "truly. But listen—there was a man walking along the path. Suddenly he yelled; a thorn had gone into his foot. He pulled out all he could, but left the point in, and then walked on his way. In a few days his foot became sore and swelled. Soon he could hardly walk. He hobbled around with a stick. His temper became vile, and his wife and children kept out of his way. He did not want his food. He didn't recover until we had pulled out the point of that thorn."

"Yoh!" said Kefa. "Bwana, what are you talking about?"

"You. There's something in you that is wrong, and you will not recover until such time as you get rid of it."

"Eee," said Kefa, and put his head in his hands. "Bwana, if you had been angry with me, it would have been all right. If you had raised your voice and said many hard things, it would have pleased me. But behold, you speak softly, and put your finger in the most uncomfortable place."

"Well, what's the trouble, old man?"

"Bwana, I have sinned. I have preached the words of God with my mouth, but my heart has been wrong. I am not strong enough. It is better for me to leave the work and return to the village, to return to witchcraft, to the drinking of much beer, and to evil living."

I had taken my pencil from my pocket and attempted to balance it on the table. Each time, it fell down with a clatter.

After the tenth time, the African dresser looked up irritably. "Don't do that, Bwana. My head aches."

I smiled. "Kefa, why doesn't the pencil stand up by itself?"

"It is not able to do so, Bwana. It is too thin," and, with a weak smile, "its legs are not strong enough."

I put my hand around it and grasped it tightly. "And now?"

"Oh," he said, "that's different. You're holding it."

"Does it fall?"

"It cannot, Bwana, because you are strong, and very much bigger than a mere pencil."

I picked up a New Testament, which had pride of place among my medical books.

"Listen, Kefa, the Book says, 'I can do all things through Christ who strengthens me.' You've been trying to do everything by yourself. You're like the pencil. You need the strong hand of God to strengthen you and help you; and don't forget that if you confess your sin to God, He will forgive you. The Lord Jesus paid the price when He was crucified, and you get the benefit."

There was a new look on the lad's face. "Oh, Bwana, you don't know how bad my sin was, or you would dismiss me from the hospital!"

"Do you think, Kefa, that God is unaware of what you have done?"

The lad hung his head.

"And do you think that if I, who am a mere man, can forgive you, God will do any less?"

He shook his head slowly; and without another word being spoken, we knelt together and prayed. What he prayed must always remain a secret.

As we stood up, he grasped my hand. "Thank you, Bwana. Truly, I understand. Now, 'I can do all things through Christ who strengthens *me*.' "

"Right. And Kefa, should you fall into trouble again, I will call you '*Kalama*' [Pencil], and you and I and God will understand."

At that moment Daudi's voice could be heard from outside, "Where's Bwana?"

"Here," I replied. "What's the matter?"

"A child, Bwana, with a broken arm. There's great trouble. The accident was three weeks ago. There's much infection through the witch doctor's work. *Yoh!* It smells!"

The last statement was so true that you merely had to follow your nose to find a small boy, with terror written in his eyes. He was clutching at his left forearm and shrank back as I approached. The back of his hand and his forearm were covered with ugly scratches, all of them infected. A nurse was gently bathing the arm with antiseptic. As we lifted him onto a table, he screamed with pain. I gave him medicine, which he was very reluctant to drink, and then made my examination. The raw swelling was an answer to those at home who had told me to leave the heathen alone because they were happy enough as they were.

Old newspapers were put on the floor; Kefa brought me plaster of paris bandages, and the powder-covered bandages sank with a gurgle into a dish of water. The small boy laughed, as he watched the bubble rise to the surface. I laughed with him.

"Behold," I said, "this is the way of wisdom. This white medicine that clings closely to the cloth is soon very, very

trong. As it dries, it develops great strength, strength
nough to keep your bones still. It is just as if we were to put
new bone outside your skin, until the old bone inside can
row strong and mend."

"*Yoh,*" said the little fellow, "does it hurt?"

I looked up at Daudi. He nodded and returned just as I
vas preparing the first bandage. On the end of the table he
ut a lump of brown sugar as big as a tennis ball, and
miling broadly, remarked, "That is the medicine we give to
oys who make no sound when they are treated."

"*Yoh,*" said the small boy, setting his teeth. Gently I
ifted the broken arm, and Kefa supported it while I put the
laster into position. Large bits of it stood out in startling
vhiteness against his black skin. His teeth were still
lenched. Another bandage was put on; I shaped it, rounded
he edges, and held it for the required five minutes to
nable it to set, and then said, "Well, did it hurt?"

"Not yet, Bwana. But have you finished?"

I adjusted the sling around his neck. "Yes, finished."

The small boy's good hand went out for the sticky-
ooking mess of sugar. His father smiled. There was an air
f cheerfulness and happiness that had not been present half
n hour before. Kefa was standing silent, wiping the plaster
f paris from the table.

Then he said, "Bwana, now I understand what you were
telling me this morning. Behold, am I not like a broken
arm? Of myself, I only produce pain; but when I am
strengthened with the power and the wisdom of God, then
the pain goes, and if I obey instructions, soon I am a useful

arm again, not to do my own wishes, but rather to serv
God."

"*Yoh,*" said the patient's father, "what's he talkin
about?"

"Let me explain, Bwana," said Kefa. "Behold, here's
chance for me to be really useful again for God."

A week went by, and there was no sign of the small boy
but a fortnight later, he returned, sling intact, but with th
plaster strangely soft. As I removed it, I asked what hap
pened.

"Behold, Bwana," he smiled, "very, very many of m
relatives arrived to visit us; and behold, they all wanted t
see this earth, which changes from powder to stone when i
is wet. They all patted it with their fingers and scratched i
with their nails; and behold, Bwana, I have many relatives!"

The plaster was off, and in the coming off, pulled som
of the hair on the lad's arm.

"*Yoh,*" he gasped, "it bites:"

I felt along the track of the bone. There, opposite th
break was a lump, where repair was going on. Daud
produced more plaster bandages, but I waved them aside.

"They're expensive things, Daudi; they're worth about a
shilling each. We can't afford to spend more than two o
three shillings on a fracture, when we have lives to save, an
quinine is so hard to get, and our stocks of the sulpha
medicines are low."

"True," said Samson, "and how badly we need needles
for injections. They cost a shilling also."

"And how long do they last you, Samson?"

"Well, Bwana, I clean them, I sharpen them, again and gain, until, behold, they are too old to use anymore."

"Bwana," said Kefa, "this boy's arm needs support. What will you do?"

In a dark corner on the top shelf of the cupboard I saw ottles of ether, each enclosed in a wrapper of corrugated ardboard. Taking one of these wrappers, I put it around his rm. Two thin pieces of tape held the cardboard in place, nd the job was complete.

"Leave that on for a week; and then the bone inside will e strong, stronger than it ever was before."

"True," said Kefa. "Something of the strength from the utside seems to be taken on by the bone inside."

I looked at him questioningly.

"Bwana, it is true what you said. Ask Jesus Christ to do , and He holds you, and holds you firmly. You feel tronger and better, and more able to do things. *Yoh,* it was good parable."

With a shy smile, the small boy went outside and eturned with a long stick of sugarcane.

"This, Bwana, is my gift to you—you who were the only ne who could help me."

I thanked him and again looked at Kefa. "Have you hown your thankfulness to God for what He has done for ou?"

Kefa shook his head. "I had forgotten that part, wana."

"Well, don't forget it any longer."

Kefa nodded and promised, "I will do all things through Christ who strengthens me."

And it was no empty promise; for that lad, although h
had ups and downs, became one of our most trusted an
effective dressers.

I talked this matter over with Daudi, and he had a
explanation. "You see, Bwana, it's like Jesus' parable
They're easy to understand, because you see them happe
and when you see God in the everyday things, then yo
remember."

7

PNEUMONIA

It doesn't often rain in Central Tanganyika, but when it does, it really pours. The heavy drops of the tropical thunderstorm beat on the tin roof of our hospital; the thunder crashed alarmingly, and the lightning for a split second turned the intense darkness into bright white light, making the hurricane lantern that was on the window ledge, seem a mere glimmer. But by that glimmer I watched a small boy lying propped up in a cot that had been made from packing cases. He was sitting up with pillows (if you can call unbleached calico filled with dry grass a pillow!) and was covered by a cotton blanket and a patchwork quilt.

His life was in the balance. Pneumonia, treated by all the devilry of the witch doctor, could easily claim his life. I expected the crisis that night.

The small boy stirred restlessly, and I saw a large white patch on that patchwork quilt with an inscription on it. I stood up and read it. "With love, from the Sunday school of St. Luke's."

It was a splendidly made quilt, and I felt that I would like to have transported for an hour that night all the folk who had stitched so industriously, making that colorful bit of bedding for our jungle hospital. I would have also liked them to be there to hear the strange sounds of an African night.

As suddenly as it had begun, the storm stopped. A hyena started its weird laughter beyond the hospital fence; from somewhere in the room came snoring, which certainly wasn't that of a child. I went to investigate, and there, underneath the bed, with her feet sticking out, was the grandmother of one of the patients. She certainly should not have been there; but at that hour of the night, you would only awaken the whole hospital if you attempted to do anything about it. Once again, the hyena howled. The little chap propped up on the pillows muttered and half opened his eyes. I looked at my watch; it was two o'clock in the morning. I would have to give him his injection very soon.

The rain had started again, and I saw a round mark suddenly appear underneath the roof in one corner. It spread down, and soon a long, reddish brown streak went down the whitewash of the wall. The fiercely driven rain had somehow soaked through, and the mud bricks were melting. I knew that this would mean more bricks to be made after the rain, and an expensive bill, which might be only five or six pounds; but five or six pounds meant a lot to us right out there in the jungle.

Suddenly there was a tremendous flash of lightning, followed almost immediately by a clap of thunder; the whole place seemed to shake. The small boy opened his eyes and screamed. I went over to him and quietened him as well as I could.

"It's all right, son; it's only a little bit of thunder."

He clung to my hand. Very gently I gave him an

injection. Quite quickly the medicine took its effect, and the small boy lost the look of strain and slipped back into quiet sleep. The long, ugly streak on the wall now extended down almost to the floor. The African night nurse came in at this stage.

"*Hongo,* Mwendwa, I think he'll sleep all right now. We have given him the medicine, and I've given him an injection to make him sleep."

"*Kah,* he may sleep here, Bwana, but he would not have slept at home."

"Why, Mwendwa, what would he have to sleep on at home?"

"Bwana, he's a small boy; he would have slept on the ground."

"But he would have had a blanket, would he not?"

"*Kah, ng'o,* he would just lie on the ground."

"And if he was sick like that?"

"Well, p'raps they would throw a cowhide to him, and he could cover himself with that; but Bwana, the children die with this disease. Do not my people say they are stabbed by some evil spirit? Behold, they have pain when they breathe. Then does not the evil spirit come and make them breathe very fast; and then, Bwana, their strength goes and they die? Then all the family wail because one of their tribe has passed over to their ancestors."

I left the hospital and walked down a long path that was running water, but ahead of me was hardly a cloud in a starlit sky. Thunderstorms just came and went with the most amazing rapidity. I thought of that small boy and wondered what would happen.

I was dog-tired and slumped into bed, but not before I had carefully tucked in my mosquito net and with a flashlight, looked around to see if any of those mosquitoes which produce more damage than the lions were about. I was not anxious to have malaria again.

A couple of moments later sleep came, that heavy solid sleep that comes when you are utterly and completely weary. It seemed to me that I had barely touched the pillow when an urgent voice outside said, *"Hodi,* Bwana, come at once; the child is on the point of death."

There was such an urgency in her voice, that for the first time in my experience, I ran to the hospital in pajamas and bathrobe. Adders and a nice collection of snakes were often on that pathway between my home and the hospital; but that night, I had no thought of snakes; I just went for my life, and for that of the small boy. In the ward he was lying in bed, panting, as a dog pants after a long run. My fingers on his pulse indicated hardly any action of his heart.

"What happened?" I gasped.

"It was the grandmother," said Mwendwa. "I went out to get some water for one of the patients. She took him out of bed and was carrying him away from the hospital, to die at the house where she lived. I just got him back."

I slipped the thermometer under the small boy's arm. Earlier in the evening, his temperature had been normal; now the thermometer read 95° F.; the crisis had occurred all right; but it had occurred apparently about the time that that wretched old woman had run off with him, taking him out into the chill of the night.

I injected a strong stimulant into his arm. Nothing

happened. Again the syringe was loaded, and the drastic measure of injecting that strong stimulant into a vein undertaken. A matter of seconds after the needle had found its mark and the plunger was pushed home, the small boy's eyes flickered. The nurse rushed in with hot water bottles. We piled him with these and with blankets. As dawn was breaking, I was able to feel his pulse going uncomfortably fast, but I felt that the danger from that old woman was past.

Suddenly from outside the hospital window came a wild screech followed by a series of yells—a sound which would have frightened anyone not used to Africa, but it brought a grin to my face. Here was a solution to my problems.

Mhutila, the water carrier, had made his first journey from the wells with ten gallons of water carried in two buckets, one suspended on each end of a pole across his shoulder. Mhutila could take the grandmother home; he would look after her very kindly but very firmly. I put my head out the window.

"Mhutila," I called.

He came over. "Bwana?"

"I have here a woman who does not obey the ways of the hospital. Will you take her home and see that she stays there?"

"Bwana," he said, "it would give me joy."

The smile that he wore on his face bore it out. And so the grandmother went home.

My doubts were dispelled three days later, when I saw my small patient sitting up in bed, as comfortable as could be, coughing a little, but with the disease well and truly in check.

"Tell me," I said, remembering the conversation I had had with the nurse a few days before, "what happened at home?"

"*Kah*, Bwana," he said, "I had no joy; behold, I thought that I was not going to lose my trouble. The pain was bad, and when I lay on the floor, the cockroaches and the *dudus* crawled on me. I couldn't sleep; and when I cried, behold, they beat me with sticks."

"What did you do?"

"Bwana, what could I do? The pain was bad. They got the witch doctor. He came along, and he scratched my ribs to let out the spirit." At that moment an old woman entered the ward, it was his grandmother. She uttered just one word, and the child suddenly became quiet, and not one more word could I get out of him, although I discovered that the witch doctor's treatment for pneumonia, apart from this scratching deeply over the ribs, was to give them a violent medicine that made them tremendously sick. What a difference it had made when he came to our hospital and when he had been given the medicine that dealt with the trouble.

A few days later we were having, as we do each morning, our staff prayers in the outpatients' room, and I saw a small boy's head appear over the windowsill. Daudi was talking about *muponyi* [the healer], and he told of Jesus, the healer of men's bodies and souls.

"*Yoh*," said the small boy. "Was it to Him you were talking the night when I nearly died?"

"Yes," I replied, "it was."

"He answered you, Bwana?"

"He did, old man, and He always does when you obey Him in everything."

8

MEDICAL MISTAKE

I focused the camera carefully.

"*Mulece kunoza cingi* [Don't do a thing], keep still!" I ordered.

The African woman with her baby on her knee looked apprehensively at the camera; the shutter clicked.

"*Yah*," said the woman, "there's no pain."

I laughed. "No, it's just that I take a picture; now turn him this way."

But as I approached the child, he struggled frantically in his mother's arms, screaming piercingly. At last I had his thigh, which was grossly swollen, in the position I wanted it. Again I pressed the button.

The African nurses and dressers standing around were in my clinical class, and I was explaining to them the various diseases and troubles from which inpatients in our hospital were suffering. I took them outside onto the veranda.

"Listen, people, all diseases grow on one of five trees." I always tried to use an analogy in describing things to my staff; it was their own line of approach. "The first tree we call *congenital*, troubles you are born with."

"*Yaaa*," said Perisi, a senior nurse, "his trouble is not that; he has only had it six weeks."

"*Heee*, but the mother told me three weeks!"

56

Perisi smiled a superior smile. "But Bwana, you are only a man, and a white one at that."

Daudi looked at me and smiled. I continued with the lecture.

"The second tree we call *inflammation*. Germs get into the body; they live there, and every twenty minutes they produce families; one germ in the morning means a tribe of them in the evening, and next day, thousands upon thousands are swarming everywhere."

The staff's eyes and mouths were wide open with astonishment.

"Aaah," said Daudi, "then it's better to kill them when they are few."

"Right," I agreed. "That's why we like to give medicine and treat wounds early."

"The next tree we call 'new growth' or *cancer*. It's a very bad thing."

The staff nodded solemnly; cancer was no rarity in Tanganyika.

"The fourth tree is called *trauma* —damage; a man is hit with a stick; a boy is attacked by a leopard; a girl bumps her toe against a stone; a woman runs a thorn into her arm; all this is *trauma*."

Again the staff nodded.

"And the fifth tree—"

"I suppose, Bwana," said Daudi, "it's the tree that the *dudus* grow on."

"Right," I replied, "we call it *parasitic* —the work of mosquitoes, fleas, ticks, and worms. So now, of these five trees, where do you find this child?"

But before we could finish the discussion, a small, panting boy arrived, "Bwana, visitors—four Bwanas in a car that shines."

Daudi grinned. "Bwana, it must be a government car."

I departed hurriedly to find the government medical officer and a famous English surgeon, who was visiting Tanganyika. They were driving through the heart of the country examining medical conditions. We drank tea under the shade of a great baobab tree, but my invitation to visit the hospital was declined because forty miles had to be traveled before sundown.

"We'll come again," said the M.O., as he waved goodbye, "and if you can come into Dodoma on Thursday we are having a special lineup of cases for Sir Thomas there."

I watched their beautiful car disappear in a cloud of dust, heading into the glare of a Westering sun, and I went back to see my little patient. What *did* that child have? I went through each classification, and every time my mind came back to the same place—cancer. But I had no X-ray machine to check it; and I was beginning to feel very futile, when, like a cool breeze, came another idea—Thursday—a special lineup of cases—Sir Thomas, the famous English surgeon. For the first time in three years, I was able to get a second opinion.

Thursday dawned; the child's thigh was tense and cold, his body was wasting rapidly; each day his ribs became more apparent. There he lay on his mother's knee in the back of the car, and we bumped our way over the roughest of roads. Nothing interested the small boy. Even three large giraffes which galloped in their queer way only a few yards in front of the car failed to bring even a light into his eyes.

There was a formidable number of sick folk for the great man to see. I felt reticent in asking him to look at my small patient, so arduous had been his day, but the famous consultant was all enthusiasm.

"Certainly I'll see him."

His skilled fingers made their examination, he took off his topee and wiped his forehead.

"What do you think?" he asked.

"My idea, Sir Thomas, is that it's cancer of the bone, a hopeless, inoperable thing."

The great man put back his spectacles, and, peering over the top, waved a forefinger at me. "I agree, I agree. There's nothing you can do but make his end painless. Too bad we couldn't have an X ray though."

With an acute feeling of disappointment, I went back to the car and drove in silence those long miles back to our jungle hospital. The mother was too shaken up by the drive to be inquisitive, and I was thankful. The small boy seemed to have improved, if anything. I walked across to Daudi's house, and there was my head dresser wrapped in a blanket with his teeth chattering.

"*Yaaa,* Bwana," said he, "I'm up the fifth tree; I have been bitten by mosquitoes. I'm in trouble; this malaria always makes my bones ache."

A series of white pills found their way, one after the other, down his throat, and to my amazement, next morning there he was, his usual, cheery self, very much on the job.

In the morning came a runner with a letter stating that

we might expect our important visitors that afternoon
Hasty arrangements were made, brooms appeared from al
quarters, scrubbing brushes were much in evidence. Ther
were many squabbling patients who objected to being
bathed again, but the staff was determined to put on a rea
show. Everybody's best uniform was put on; the beds hac
never been better made, and I was amused to see Daud
driving away some relations he did not feel would adc
anything in the way of background to the hospital.

I arranged for the cooks to demonstrate their art.

The pathology room was in apple-pie order.

The dispensary gleamed with great bottles, full ol
medicines each of a different color. In fact the hospital was
at its very best.

I made arrangements. "Daudi, you do any routine work
that comes in. I want you to syringe out the ears of the
patient in number four bed, do the blood slides from the
children's ward, and any other routine jobs."

The next hours were full. I have seldom had a more
interesting day.

I watched that famous London surgeon sitting back in
my armchair, which, had he known it, a year before was a
mere packing case, and listened to him telling of some of his
amazing experiences. There was a sound of laughter and of
a bouncing ball outside.

"The staff is going to play football with the village this
afternoon, sir; would you care to come and see science
triumph?"

The great man came and watched with interest, as those
nimble Africans, barefooted, played amazingly good foot-

all. The shadows were lengthening as we turned for home
just in time to meet Daudi.

He spoke in Chigogo and gave me his report. "All is
well, Bwana, in the men's ward. The child with malaria of
the brain is just the same, and I have fixed up the little boy
with the abscess."

In English I said, "The little boy with the abscess?"

Daudi replied in the same language, "Yes, sir, the one in
bed number two."

"What? That's the child with cancer."

"No, Bwana, a big abscess of the thigh."

"Oh no, Daudi, Sir Thomas had clinched that particular
point; the poor little fellow has cancer; he can't survive."

Daudi's face was a picture. "No, Bwana, it's an
abscess."

"What do you mean?" the great man asked.

"Sir," said Daudi, "have I done wrong? But the Bwana
said when you had a swelling and were in doubt, put in a
needle. I put in a needle, Bwana, and found pus; so I drew it
off with a large needle, nearly a pint of it, and the germ is the
green one you call *pyocyaneus.*"

"Thank you, Daudi, I will come and see him later."

My African dresser departed on the double. To my
considerable relief, the eminent surgeon's sides were
shaking with laughter. "What a story!" he said. "What a
story to tell my colleagues at home! The medical profession
has had its eye wiped by an African male nurse!"

Later that evening, I was discussing the case around the
campfire with the hospital lads. "You see," I explained, "it
was a deep abscess, hard to get at, but it was killing the

small boy. I thought it was this trouble called cancer; the great one thought so too; we both were sincere but wrong. The real cause was found when one followed the way the book teaches."

"*Yah*," said Samson, "isn't it like the abscess of men's souls, those hidden things? Many wise ones say, 'There is no way out of sin,' of things like bad thoughts, and they nurse grievances, pride, and ugly actions; but we know differently."

"What does the Good Book say, Samson?"

"It says, Bwana, and Jesus says it, 'I am the way, the truth and the life.' "

A week went by, and I watched the radiant mother playing with her small, healthy boy. As I came up, she smiled. "Bwana, look at him; you have taken away the thing that was killing him."

"Yes," I replied, "but I wonder if you in your heart have got something tucked away, something that has not been forgiven by the Son of God?"

The smile faded from her face. "Bwana," she said, "I like doing those things; I like them too much to give them up; they don't give pain; they satisfy me."

"But when you are old," I asked, "what then?"

"*Yah*," she laughed, "I am not yet old; there will be time to think of that later."

"Wrong," I replied. "God says, 'Now is the time.' "

She was one of the many about whom it would never be certain which way they decided.

9

SORE THUMB

I stood on the steps of my jungle home in Central Tanganyika and looked beyond the thornbush, which was matted up almost to the veranda, beyond it, to a group of baobab trees, which reached right down to the plain as far as the eye could see. Along a winding path, showing white against the red soil, came a figure, moving at a brisk pace and carrying over his shoulders two great cone-shaped baskets. I turned to my cook, Timothy, "Look, Tim, here comes Matayo. We'll have some papaws now."

Tim laughed. "Bwana, if ever there was *mpiligazi* [a hard worker] it was that man Matayo. He lives right over there—" He pointed with his chin toward a granite boulder-covered mountainside, six or seven miles away, "at Chikuyu, the place of fig trees, and behold, he has a very good garden. He works very hard. Not only that, Bwana, but he is the Christian teacher in that village. He will not receive one cent for the work that he does; he prefers to work in his garden and sell his fruit."

"Well, Tim, it suits me. When old Matayo comes and sells me his fruit, it means that we have all the papaws that we need. And believe me, Tim, here in Tanganyika you want to eat as much fruit and vegetables as you possibly can."

"*Kah*, Bwana, if you have *ugali* [porridge] that's a[l]
that's required. Are not our people well developed?"

"No," I said, "they're not. Look at that child playin[g]
out in the sun." The little fellow was obviously sufferin[g]
from rickets. "He should have been given fat as well a[s]
porridge. He wasn't given milk, Timothy, and behold, he'[s]
got a disease we call 'rickets.' He needs to have all sorts o[f]
other things, not just porridge, as you do."

"*Kah*, but the cows here don't give much milk, Bwana."

"No, that's true, but you ought to give the children ever[y]
drop you can get."

Matayo was coming close now. My cook boy came ou[t]
from the kitchen. His job was to split the wood and clean th[e]
pots. When he saw Matayo, he gave a shrill whistle
Generally Matayo followed suit, but not this time
Generally too, when he got to within a hundred yards of th[e]
kitchen, he would put on a final spurt and finish up with [a]
peculiar little song, all his own. That day he didn't.

As he came close I saw there was a haggard look abou[t]
him. He took the very dilapidated felt hat from his head
and as he did so, I saw that his right hand was tied up wit[h]
an old piece of khaki material.

"*Mbukwa*, Matayo. How are you?" I asked.

"*Heh*, Bwana, I haven't the smallest bit of joy."

"That doesn't sound like you, Matayo, what'[s]
happened?"

"*Kah*, Bwana, my hand. *Heh!* For days and days, it'[s]
just been aching and aching and aching, and I can't sleep
Bwana. *Kumbe*, it's an awful feeling, and I decided that [I]
couldn't stand it any longer; so I have come to you."

"Good, we'll see what we can do for you. Leave your papaws here, and let's go up to the hospital."

I produced a shilling, which was the price of one of these splendid baskets full of fruit the size of a football. Matayo rummaged with his left hand in the second basket, and pulled out six green limes the size of golf balls and presented them to me. "Bwana, these are for you, and two corn cobs." Corn does not usually grow at that time of the year, but Matayo had planted a few grains and had carefully tended them, knowing my weakness for sweet corn.

Carefully carrying his other basket of papaws, he came with me to the hospital. In a few minutes the patients and dispensers had bought all his fruit and were sitting in the shade of the thorn trees consuming them.

I sat Matayo down on a box in the shade, shook down a thermometer, and placed it under his tongue. Of course, no sooner had it been placed there, than he wanted to talk.

"Be quiet" I said. "You must keep that under your tongue for a few minutes, and then we'll hear the story you have to tell."

I felt his pulse at the same time. It had the weak, fast type of beat, which is characteristic of a fever. I took the thermometer from his mouth.

"Kah," he said, "what a relief to be able to talk."

I looked at the silver line of mercury—101°. Removing the piece of cloth from his hand, I saw the cause of the whole trouble. Just at the base of his thumb, and the normal swollen portion of the hand, was a large swelling. The whole thing was about three times its normal size. I touched it; it was acutely tender. Then I tried to move the thumb, but

again there was intense pain. Carefully I examined the oth
fingers, the palm of his hand, the back, his elbow, and I fe
the glands under his arms. I nodded my head.

"Matayo, we can help you all right, but you're going t
be in the hospital, oh, perhaps a week."

"Kah," he replied, "who will look after my garden?"

"Who will look after your hand, if anything goes wron
What value is there in a man whose hand will not work
especially if it is his right hand?"

He shook his head. "Bwana, your words are wise; carr
on. I would like you to give me the pills that take away th
pain, that my hand may get better. *Kah,* Bwana, it throb
muno muno [very much]."

"Matayo, my friend, there is little value in giving yo
pills to take away the throbbing feeling. They might stop th
pain for a little while, but they would not stop the damag
that is going on inside your hand. Unless I remove fro
inside your hand all the trouble that is there, behold, yo
will have a hand that is no value to you at all."

Daudi was standing beside me. "Bwana, I don't suppos
Matayo has been able to do any work for many days."

"Kah," said Matayo, "for three days now, I have no
been able to do any work."

Daudi said, "Just because of your hand?"

Matayo nodded. "Just because of my hand, *heh,* ju
because of my hand, and nor would you; the pain was ther
throbbing, throbbing, throbbing."

"Yes, it was because of that in your hand?" I asked.

"Yes," said Matayo, "yes, yes!"

"There, Daudi, you have the answer to the question tha

you asked me yesterday. You asked why it is that God sometimes does not answer prayer. And here is your answer. If you will look in God's Book, you will read, 'If I regard iniquity in my heart, the Lord will not hear me.' Now that means agreeing in your mind to do something that is wrong and that is sinful; even if you don't actually do the thing, it's agreeing in your mind that matters. Do you understand me?"

"Heh," Daudi nodded slowly.

"Well, when your mind is in that state, then God does not hear your prayer, and it is necessary to clear away from your mind the thing that is wrong before your prayers *are* heard. Just in the same way as it is required to take from Matayo's hand the thing that is causing the trouble there before he will be able to be useful in life again."

The two African Christians in front of me nodded their heads.

"Heeeh, we see, Bwana."

"Matayo," I went on, "when did you last have anything to eat?"

"Bwana," he replied, "I have not been able to eat."

"Nothing at all? Not even a papaw?"

"Oh well, Bwana, two or three of those."

I looked at those large fruits and saw that what he thought was "nothing at all" was not quite the same as my idea of it!

About four hours later he came to the operating room. Daudi had opened a bottle of anesthetic, and everything was scrubbed up and ready.

"Bwana, before you give me the medicine of sleep, sho me what you are going to do."

I took his good hand and showed it to him.

"Are you going to cut me?"

"Yes," I said, holding his palm upward; and turning around, I looked at the back of his hand. "If you cut into th palm of the hand, even if it is only a little bit, it is dangerou You might cut nerves; you might cut arteries; so you go t the back of the hand; you find the bone of the first finge you make a small cut there, and you take out the troubl that is in the hand, through that hole. In that way, there no danger of hurting the nerves of the hand."

"*Kah*, if I'd been doing it, I would have just made a c in the closest place, Bwana."

"Yes, Matayo, you would, and you would have done lot of damage. You see, my medical books tell me just wha is the best way to do it. Many doctors give their experienc that is how you know."

"*Heeh*, Bwana, there is always a right way and a wron way."

"Truly, you remember what Solomon said in his book *Zinhandaguzi* [Proverbs]? Did he not say, 'There is a wa that seemeth right unto a man, but the end thereof are th ways of death'? You see, you would ruin your hand if yo went your own way. Let us follow the way of wisdom."

Just before he had the anesthetic, we bowed our head and asked Almighty God to help us to follow the way o wisdom, not only in surgery, but in life.

A few drops of anesthetic were put on a mask. A fe

minutes later he was breathing deeply. In a matter of a few seconds the abscess in his hand was opened.

"*Kumbe!*" said Daudi, "that will be better."

"*Ahhhh,*" said Matayo next morning, "that is better, Bwana."

The swelling progressively went down. Before long, Matayo, with his hand bandaged, and with a pot of ointment in his large cone-shaped basket, instead of his papaws, was wending his way back through the baobab trees to the little mission school on the side of the granite boulder-studded hill, the place where the fig trees were; and I knew that the people of that village would hear again of the way, the truth and the life, the Son of God, who makes all the difference to men's lives, whether they be black or white.

10

BEESTING

The white nurse, called "Sister," had been out visiting contacting people who had been in our hospital, seein mothers and babies, and checking up on the arrangement for baby in the various houses. In the cool of the morning she had walked to an outlying village five miles away, an had come into a particularly squalid dwelling to see an ol woman with chronic arthritis. As she talked and examine the old woman by the light of the fire which burned in th center of the hut, she heard a moan come from further bac in the gloom behind the great storage bins, where the grai was kept. Picking up a lighted stick, she walked toward th place from which the sound came, and there, on a cowhid lay a young woman, her face and body grossly swollen, an beside her a three-month-old baby. Sister at once sent th African nurse who was with her, back to our hospital, an two hours later I drove my ancient Ford over dry riverbed and unmade roads, to the spot. We carefully lifted the youn woman onto a mattress in the back, and soon she was in be and being gently sponged with warm water. Her pain wa intense; so intense that not until a sizeable dose of morphine had been given, could we get the story of what had happene to her.

Treatment was the first essential, and I asked Sister t

do it. Armed with a small pair of forceps and a bowl of lotion, she set to work on a job which kept her busy till sundown. Upon my return, I found the patient comfortably dressed in hospital nightdress, looking really amusing—her black skin showing up in patches through a liberal application of calamine lotion. Her baby chuckled delightedly in a cot at the end of her bed. Hilda, an African nurse, had just put him down and was washing the milk bottle that she had finished using.

"Yoh!" she said, "he is a darling child. He is worth all his mother did for him."

I frowned. "I don't understand."

Sister looked up from bandaging a badly inflamed ankle. "She lives at Manhambulu and was looking after her potato garden among the baobab trees near the river."

Hilda interrupted, "Tell him, Bibi, that this is a country of much *oochi* [honey]."

Sister nodded. "In the trees above her were many hives." She smiled at me; for once, in the early days, I had inquired if these long coffin-like affairs high up in the trees were a tribal custom of burial!

"It appears," went on Sister, "that some small boys with slings were trying out their skill; and apparently there was no doubt about their aim, for they brought down one of those great hives with a bump. The boys were horrified, and ran as fast as they could, for two reasons: they feared both the bees and their father's wrath! But Semwa here could not get away quickly enough, and the bees swarmed around her to bite her. She ran as fast as she could, but the bees flew faster. The baby screamed in terror, and Semwa, not

thinking of herself, tore off her cloth and wrapped it around
the baby, and was herself bitten all over. But the baby
escaped. She ran till she was exhausted, and then fell in a
faint beside the path. There her relatives found her. They
picked her up and carried her to her hut, and there she lay in
the dark, moaning from the effect of hundreds of stings, and
she only had one thing to say, 'The baby is safe, and without
even one sting. I suffered, so that he might be safe.' "

"Semwa," I said, "those are almost the words that Jesus
used. He said, 'I am come that they might have life, and that
they might have it more abundantly.' "

"Who is Jesus?" asked Semwa.

I nodded across to Hilda. "She'll tell you." Then I
asked, "Why did you do it? Why did you pull your own
cloth off and cover him?"

"*Yoh!*" she replied. "I did that because I love him. I did
not want him to die or to suffer pain. I wanted him to live, to
grow." She held out her bandaged hands to the smiling
child.

"But he doesn't understand. He doesn't know what
you've done for him," I said, pretending to protest.

"*Yoh,* he is only a baby, and would I not do this for him,
whether he understood it or not?"

I looked at Hilda. She had been taking it all in and
nodded.

In the record book, in pencil above her name, I wrote the
figure "7." I felt that in seven days' time all would be well;
she would be fit to go home. Beestings, while they are
uncomfortable, are little else. I was wrong.

After two days, Semwa's temperature soared up. She

went into a wild delirium and raved. It was a strange sort of a complaint and called for drastic treatment. By every means available, we forced fluids into her body. Day after day, Hilda sat beside her, working and putting everything she knew from the nursing angle into helping that unfortunate woman.

Now, Hilda and I had a standing joke. Sometimes after a night up in the operating room, or in the maternity ward, she would say to me, "Bwana, behold, you have black circles around your eyes."

One morning I came into the ward, and found Hilda struggling with Semwa. We quietened our patient, and I looked at Hilda. She had fatigue written on every feature.

"*Yoh!*" I said. "Behold, you've got black circles around your eyes."

An answering smile came. "*Yoh*, Bwana, but I am tired. I have not seen the inside of a blanket for two days or two nights.

"Well, go to bed," I ordered.

The African nurse shook her head. "This woman's my charge. I have prayed that she would live, and God expects you not only to pray, but to work. I have asked Him for strength; and behold, I will carry on."

The next day, Semwa was very weak, but definitely around the corner. Hilda sat beside her, with a beaming smile. She stretched and yawned.

"Behold, Bwana, now I can go to sleep." She patted her patient's bandaged hand and pointed to the baby. "He is all right. I fed him. I made all his milk. I bathed him. All is well. Now rest."

Late that afternoon I heard a song coming from the nurses' bathroom, and in a few minutes Hilda appeared in a clean uniform.

Yoh!" she said, "I am better now. Behold, I am going to read to the woman whose life has been my responsibility."

"Truly," I said, "because of your work, she lived."

"Bwana," she said, "if Jesus loved me so much that He Himself bore my sins in His own body on the cross, how much more should I show my thankfulness to Him by helping this woman, who has never even heard of Him."

When I went to see how her infected bites were getting on, Semwa told me what she had heard.

"Bwana, Hilda says that what I did for my baby is a very small picture of what Jesus did for me. I suffered pain and risked death for him. But He was beaten for our sins. They put thorns around His forehead, and then killed Him; and Hilda says that all this happened so that we could have life forever."

"That's true. That's true."

This all happened at four o'clock. At seven that evening, an agitated voice came at the door. "Bwana, Semwa has disappeared." Her bed was empty. Her clothes were still in the cupboard. The baby was gone.

And then came news. Her husband and some of his relations, who, Daudi said, were hard men, had been seen skulking around behind the hospital at sundown.

Next day the secret was out. She had been dragged from her bed while the nurses were at tea, and her relatives had taken her miles away into the bush. They felt that she had been bewitched, and at the advice of the witch doctor, all of whose medicines had been ineffective, they had come stealthily by night and kidnapped her.

Months went by, and no news of Semwa came to us. I was talking to Hilda one day about it all, and she said, "Well, Bwana, I have still one way of helping her. Each day I ask God to be with her, and I ask that the words and the things we did may just speak to her heart; that, as she looks at her baby, she may think of what we said and of what we did."

Famine had stricken the country. We drove out miles into unexplored parts, taking food and medicines. It was a terrible task in one way, to see women and children—mere creatures of skin and bones—faintly endeavoring to keep the birds from their wretched crops, which were only half their proper height because of the failure of the rains.

One woman attracted my attention. I felt certain I had seen her somewhere. As we dealt out basins of grain to the people, they thronged around us, but she waited till last.

"Bwana," she said, "may I return with you to the hospital? My husband is dead. My two babies have died from famine. Perhaps I could work in the hospital."

"Have you ever been there?" I asked. "Do you know how hard the work is?"

"No, but I know it is a good place."

"But are you going because you know there is food there?"

"I am going, Bwana, because I want to learn what a woman in this village learned."

It was getting late in the day, and so I told her to bring her goods. All she had was tied up in a cloth and was no

bigger than a plum pudding. She got into the back and sa
down with Hilda, and we drove home over the plains.

The marvel of an East African sunset spread before me
as I dodged trees and the scars of soil erosion. The red
faded to purples and to deep greens, and the stars twinkled
out. The baobab trees in full leaf loomed up on each side
and as darkness fell, we stopped to have a cup of tea.

As I pumped the primus, Hilda said to me, "Bwana, you
remember Semwa?"

"Truly," I replied. "The beesting woman."

"She died only yesterday at that village, from
starvation, and her baby before her. But Bwana, what we
told her in the hospital had stuck. Behold, she has told
others of Jesus. She told them how she had saved her baby's
life and then of how Jesus had endured the cross and
despised the shame and died to give her everlasting life."

"Was it worth it, Hilda? To stay up night after night
and to know now, that some day, not only will we meet our
Saviour face to face, but we will meet those of our friends
whom we have helped in our hospital here?"

Hilda nodded. "It's worth a few sleepless nights, Bwana.
It's worth almost anything to sow good seeds for Him."

11

BEER AND BURNS

"Yes," said Daudi, "we had a famine last year, and the crops were very bad, and everybody prayed to God and were very sorry for their sins when their stomachs were empty; but this year, *heeh,* the rains were good, the crops were good, everybodys's grain bins are full of corn, and very few people even remembered God.

"In fact, instead of storing up corn against the next famine, they are turning it all into beer. The village reeks of home brew, and before long the cemetery will be enlarged; men will break other men's heads when they are drunk; we will spend all the night operating, repairing damage done by a man full of beer with a spear in his hand. *Yah!*" He spat forcefully.

"I take it therefore, Daudi, that you don't agree with those who drink beer."

Daudi looked at me. "There was a time, Bwana, when I drank lots. They call it food, and truly it is food for headaches and heartaches. *Heeh.*"

He spat again, and I could see that he was just about to break into a further tirade against what the locals called *wujimbi.* But at that moment we heard children's voices; it was not the usual laughing chatter of little people—there was fear and urgency in the sound.

"The Bwana's in there," said one of them, and then heard, *"Hodi, hodi* [May I come in]?"

Two small girls were on the veranda, the taller of the was seven. On her back she carried a two-year-old bo screaming with pain. Her smaller sister was trying to g him safely to the ground. The little girl who had bee carrying him looked utterly weary, and both the sisters wer in great distress. Carefully I lifted the baby down and p him on our examination table. As I did so, I saw he wa covered with blisters, red raw in places where the skin ha rubbed off while he was being carried to the hospital.

Both the little girls had squatted on the floor, and wer crying. Daudi ran off for tannin jelly, while I gave the bab an injection to ease his pain. Carefully I measured th amount of morphine necessary, blew the air out of th syringe, and injected. The baby screamed still louder. turned to the elder of the two. "What is your name?" asked.

"Marita, Bwana."

"Tell me, Marita, how did he get burned?"

At that moment Daudi walked in, just in time to hear th small girl say, *"Yeh,* Bwana, he was scalded when a clay po of *wujimbi* broke as he was crawling on the ground, and i went all over him."

"Kah," said Daudi, "and why did they send you wit the child?"

The five-year-old sister, whose name we discovered late was Pepitua, answered like a shot out of a gun, *"Kah,* wer they not all drunk?"

"What," said Daudi, "at this hour of the morning?"

"Yah," replied the small girl, "have they recovered from what they drank last night?"

"And we," said Marita, "do we not go to the mission kindergarten, and have we not drunk the medicine of the hospital for our coughs? So we said, 'We will take him up to the Bwana; he will help us.' "

"But," said Daudi, "will not your people be very angry?"

"Yoh!" replied Marita, "will he not die unless you help?"

While we were speaking, treatment had been given to the little fellow. I am always afraid, desperately afraid, of burns in children. There are few more dangerous things.

"Daudi," I said, "we must prepare for a blood transfusion, since blood transfusions are lifesaving with little people who get burned. Go down to that house and get the relations; take the chief with you if you wish, and make all the trouble in the world as long as you get some half a dozen people willing to give their blood."

Hilda, the ward nurse, by this time had the baby comfortable and lying in a cot, on the end of which was inscribed, "In loving memory of John, age 5." As I looked at that white-veiled nurse and her small, shocked patient, I would have given much to have had standing beside me the one who, year by year, donated the ten pounds necessary to support the cot, which meant a score of lives saved each year.

"Bwana, all that the children said was true; they are all drunk, hopelessly drunk; not one of them is able even to walk, and they are all refusing to come."

"Bwana," said Marita, "cannot we help? Do we not lov our little brother?"

"Listen, children, what we want is some blood from some well person to run into your little brother's veins."

"Bwana," replied the little girl, "you can have some o mine; I'm not frightened."

"Bwana," said Daudi, "try mine."

"We can't do it, Daudi. I once gave some of my blood o a job like this, and I was dizzy all the time I was operating We cannot be the blood bank as well as the hospital staf There are other lives depending on us."

The small girl behaved like a veteran. She did not flinc as I made the tests, nor when I took half a pint of bloo from her arm, but as I bandaged up her arm, she suddenl fainted from sheer tiredness, as well as blood lack. We pi her into the cot next to her little brother, with five-year-ol Pepitua sitting on a three-legged stool between then watching open-eyed, as very carefully we ran her sister' blood into her baby brother.

Halfway through this proceeding, I heard a murmur c voices outside. Daudi was laying down the law to somebod in no uncertain terms.

"*Yah,*" whispered Pepitua, "it is the voice of m father." She huddled up into a corner. "He's very *ka* [fierce]. He beats us when he's drunk."

Daudi came to the door. "The father is here, Bwana." And in English, "He's almost sober, but don't speak wit him; he's not worth the words."

Over his shoulder peered the unkempt head of a African I knew quite well. He had been one of m

uarrymen when we got the stone to build the hospital
ards.

"Bwana," said Daudi again in English, "when he speaks
o you, don't reply. Let him realize how great is his trouble
nd his sin."

It was a very chastened man to whom I spoke later that
vening.

"Nhete," I said, "you have two grand little daughters.
Iarita is as brave as a lion. They have saved your small
on's life, while you snored like a hog."

"Kah," said Daudi, his tone oozing disgust.

"But Bwana, I did not know."

"Of course you didn't" said Daudi, "and you didn't
are. Oh, get out, don't let us see you till tomorrow. You
eek of beer."

Back in the ward I found both my little patients
omfortable and out of danger,

Next morning, Daudi had an idea. "Bwana, let us go and
isit that part of the country where these people live. I have
oubts."

So had I, as we walked that evening through a belt of
actus to the village.

"There's a man here," said Daudi, "whose name is
umbo."

"Why, he was one of my masons," I replied.

"Yes, Bwana, and I have heard that his wife Abegeli,
akes large quantities of beer at his house, and I think it
as his beer that made these people drunk. Behold, they
ere only cooking their own; it would not be ready for
rinking for some days."

At that moment we came out onto a clearing, a
directly in front of us, smiling blandly, was Tumbo.

"*Mbukwa,* Bwana."

I greeted him and then got right down to busine
"Tumbo, I hear you have been brewing beer."

"Bwana, I? Your chief mason—brew beer? Me? N
Bwana."

"*Kah,* you are full of words."

"Well," said Tumbo, "if you don't believe me, come a
look; search my house."

"*Yah,*" said Daudi, in English, "did they not know
were coming; is not everything hidden?"

"Oh, I thought of that, Daudi, and I have brought n
flashlight."

Tumbo had already reached the door of his house a
was standing aside for us to come in.

"Search, Bwana, everywhere, you will not find it in n
house."

My flashlight lighted every corner of that dim mu
roofed, mud-walled, mud-floored African house. I saw t
cowhides that they used for beds; I almost stepped on
hen's nest, containing four eggs. There was a pile of straw
a corner, which Daudi moved.

"*Heh,*" smirked Tumbo, "is there beer there?"

But I noticed he walked past a large wickerwork gra
bin. Stopping, I shone my light into this.

"Just grain, Bwana," he said, "just grain."

Daudi prodded the millet with his stick, and a hollo
sound resulted.

"*Yeh,*" said Daudi, "what's that?"

"Oh nothing," said Tumbo, "nothing at all."

Daudi scraped the grain away and revealed two ten-gallon clay pots full of beer.

"Yah," said Daudi, his eyebrows almost in his hairline.

"Well," said Tumbo, "that shows you what people will do. What a mean trick, hiding their pots of beer in my house."

"You really did not know those pots were there?" I asked.

"No," replied Tumbo, "I had no idea. They had no business whatsoever to put them there."

"And you don't want the beer?" I asked.

"No," said Tumbo, "certainly not."

"Kah," said Daudi, "if it doesn't belong to you, and you don't want it, you don't mind dumping it out?"

"Ah no-o-o," said Tumbo, carrying on manfully, "it will—it will—teach them a good lesson—whoever—put it here—"

A minute later the air reeked with the smell of spilled beer.

As we walked back to the hospital, Daudi said, "It is very true, Bwana, that your sin will find you out; but it seems very tragic when, because of your sin, little people suffer."

"Truly, Daudi," I said, "sin is a foul thing; it takes away our hope of eternal life, and it hurts others all along the way."

12

FAIR, FAT, AND FORTY

"It often happens," said Daudi, who was giving a lecture on primus stoves. "Now watch."

He got to work with the pump. "As surely as—" At that moment, kerosene squirted out through the burner and a sheet of flame three feet high shot into the air. One of the junior dressers, in his excitement, lost his balance and fell backward off the three-legged stool, to the accompaniment of grins from the staff of our hospital. There was a hiss, and Daudi opened the valve and the flames died down.

"As surely as you are in too much of a hurry," said Daudi, "you get into trouble. Wait until the machine is hot, until the blue flame is small, *then* pump, not before; go gently. And do not only go gently when you are using a machine, but when you deal with men. Do not let your anger flare up. Does not God's Book say, 'A soft answer turns away wrath'?" He waited this time until the flame was small; then he pumped gently, and the whole machine harmoniously did his bidding.

A voice was heard just outside the door. *"Nomucema Bwana, lulu baha* [I will call the doctor at once]."

The African nurse on duty was in a state of high excitement. "They've brought a cow," she said, "a good cow."

I looked through the window and saw a rather skinny bull. All bulls are cows to the Africans, who think of them either as the price of their dowry when they belong to themselves or, if they belong to other people, a very cheerful addition to the diet.

"*Yoh,*" said Daudi, "do you look only at the cow? Is there not a sick person?"

"*Mbeka,*" replied the girl, "truly, there's a sick one. It is the chief, the *mupembamoto,* from right over there." She pointed with her chin and her voice became squeaky, showing it was miles away. Then, with a giggle, "He's awfully fat, and he's making a dreadful noise, but his *karani* [clerk] says that he will give the Bwana the cow straightaway, if only he can stop the pain."

There was very real interest stirred, and I couldn't help feeling that they expected me to turn on medical science, not only to save the discomfort of a very plump chief, but also they had thoughts of a campfire and a feast.

Daudi already had the chief lying on two benches put side by side under the shade of a pepper tree, and soon we were surrounded by an admiring throng. As I walked up, one of the Africans who had come with the chief, said, "*Yoh,* he's a weight. Did it not take six of us to carry him? *Nhembo* [The elephant] is his relation, and Bwana, does he make a noise? He says *uk!* and *eee!* and then he screams and froths at the mouth."

"What do you think, Daudi?"

"Does he bite his tongue?" asked the African.

"No," came the answer.

"Then, Bwana, I don't think it is epilepsy."

"But," said the African ambulance man, if you coul call him such, "he draws his knees up, clasps his hands ove his stomach and groans, and the noise he makes!" He shoo his head, and I grinned, thinking of what I had learned i my medical school—fair, fat, and forty, the signposts to particularly uncomfortable disease. When I saw my patien he certainly was fat and he probably was forty, but he wa black as coal.

I was struck by the fact that his eyes did not shine whit as they normally do from a black face. There he lay with vast crowd of everybody looking on. When I attempted t shoo them away, Daudi said, "It's all right, Bwana, he like this." So I continued my examination in what looked like glorified football huddle.

My fingers felt around in the rolls of his ample midriff When they reached the area under his ribs on the right-han side, he let out a yell that sent the small boys scurrying fo cover.

"Ah!" I said, "there we are, Daudi. Look at hi eyes—they're yellow. See where his pain is. He's go gallstones."

I wrote on a piece of paper orders for a particular type o injection. Daudi hurried off to prepare it. We carried ou bulky patient off to the ward, and I was amused to see them get six gasoline cans to support the frame of the bed. With grunt, the chief sank down upon it, and with a grunt th ropes of the mattress stretched to their limit. Daud appeared with a syringe.

"Now, great one, your pain will go quickly with on injection." For five minutes he lay there, making all th doleful sounds imaginable, and then they gradually eased off into sighs of comfort, and he even attempted to sit up.

"Chief," I said, "I have merely covered up your pain."

"I don't care, Bwana, it's gone."

"But it will come back again."

Turning to his retinue he said, "Give the Bwana the cow."

The words were no sooner out of his mouth, than a secret signal went from Daudi, and I learned afterward that within five minutes, the unfortunate animal was dead and being cut up into chunks. My staff were afraid that the chief might change his mind.

I ordered various other treatments, including a hot brick wrapped in an old piece of blanket—our local equivalent to a hot-water bottle, and I left my now beaming patient with this burden reposing elegantly along his equator.

Daudi had everything organized. As I went outside the ward, I found that Samson was cutting off lumps of steak, and James had a whole hindquarter over his shoulders. The nurses had all demanded their particular bit, while the schoolgirls were hastily collecting firewood for a bonfire and the Tangayikan modification of a barbecue. Suddenly they all burst into song, one of their favorite cultivating songs, with its rhythm making you almost hear hoes digging deep into moist soil.

They didn't sing it once but half a dozen times, altering the words to fit in with the various bits of meat that they had; and as I walked home in the sunset, I could still hear the strains. I watched the crows overhead and the small boys driving home the cattle. A few lonely-looking cornstalks of last year's crop stuck up here and there in the dryness and brownness of this Central African plain, and always as a background came the joyful voices of my staff and the girls' school.

It was now after dark. I changed my shorts for a thick pair of mosquito-proof trousers and long leather boots that protected my ankles and submitted myself to being sprayed with a crude form of mosquito repellent that we had made from kerosene and derris root.

There must have been at least one hundred Africans waiting for the fire to be lit. They had sticks of all lengths and each one had his own little bit of meat that he was going to roast. On a long piece of fencing wire was the main morsel of the evening, put so that it would swing to and fro like a pendulum along the length of the fire. I struck a match, lighted the dry grass, and in a minute the flames were leaping, the meat sizzling, and the crowd of Africans singing.

Song followed song, stories very like Aesop's fables were told until a voice called, "Cooked!" For quite a time there was silence, broken only by appreciative noises and the sound of teeth dealing with meat.

In the middle of it came a call. "Bwana, come quickly, the chief is yelling with pain again."

I hurried off and spent a long time explaining to the fat African chief that what he needed was to have the cause of his trouble removed. The injection did nothing but quieten the pain for a time. I dealt with his pain again and gave orders for preparation for his operation the next morning and went back to the feast.

Daudi was talking to a very contented group of people. A pile of bones in the middle of the fire was mute evidence of their enjoyment of the cow.

Coming through the warm African night, I heard my head dispenser's voice, "The chief wanted his pain stopped; he rejoiced when it happened but sorrowed when the pain returned. Remember, it is not enough to be sorry because God punishes you for sin, it is necessary to ask Him to cure the cause. Remember His own words, 'Him that comes to me I will under no circumstances cast out.' "

I came into the light of the embers. "Isn't that true, Bwana?" asked Daudi.

"It is indeed. Why, He did it for me."

13

MASAI

As we came through the glaring sun, in Equatorial Africa
we saw a long line of folk walking along the narrow path
that came up past the little church to the hospital. They were
all very tall, very lithe people; they didn't walk in the way
which is usual with the people of this country, nor did they
look black somehow, but the sun seemed to shine on them
redly.

"*Kah*," said Daudi. "They are Masai, the tribe who
come up from near Mt. Kilimanjaro. They are very fierce,
Bwana; do they not live on their cattle? Did not our tribe
fight with them in the days that have gone? They are people
of trouble."

Oh, they'll be all right, Daudi; they have come along for
medicine, and when people are sick they don't generally
make trouble."

"*Huh!*" The dispenser raised his eyebrows. "Do you
think they're all sick, or do you think they've just brought
one person along? Will they not demand this and demand
that? Will they not say that they want this medicine and that
medicine? Will they not—"

"*Kah*, cheer up, Daudi; it won't be as bad as all that. At
any rate, we'll do all we can for them."

"They're people that mean trouble, Bwana. For

instance, they will not eat the food of the hospital; they do not eat porridge; they eat their own sort of food."

"What's that?"

Daudi's nose wrinkled delicately. "They do not eat porridge as we do, but milk mixed with the blood of the cow that they have milked. *Yah,* think of it!"

"But surely they eat other things?"

"No, Bwana, that is their food."

"Well, we can't give it to them here."

"No, Bwana, that's why I say they are people who bring trouble, and then, Bwana, they'll refuse to be washed; they do not wash in water like we do; they rub themselves with sour milk or with fat from a cow."

It didn't sound very attractive to me, but as we came closer I saw that they were very graceful people indeed, and were dressed in the most ornate fashion. The women carried on their backs great long gourds holding about two gallons of milk. They preferred it sour, made sour in a way which I didn't find particularly entertaining. The women wore the most amazing ornaments; their arms had big spirals of copper and silvered wire that went from their wrists to their elbows, and around their necks were huge spirals of wire. Their ears were full of bead ornaments, and I noticed that the men all carried six-foot spears; and strapped to their sides were long red leather scabbards, holding knives that were about two to three feet long.

"Kah," whispered Daudi, "didn't I tell you the Masai are the people of trouble?"

"Trouble or no trouble," I said, "we're going to help them if we can."

So I came forward to greet them, and in my best
Chigogo I said,

"*Mbukwa* Good morning, everybody."

But they just shook their heads, and one of them turned
around to me and said, "*Jambo,* Bwana."

I discovered that apart from their own language, which
was entirely beyond me, they spoke only Swahili. Now, I
knew Swahili in a sort of a way, and so our conversation
continued. It appeared that they had brought in a young
man who was suffering from vague pains.

I couldn't quite understand what the pains were, but
Daudi, beside me, said in English, "Bwana, I know what
this trouble is. It is a bad thing indeed; it comes from living
in the wrong way."

"We'll get him into the ward and examine him."

Now our first trouble started. The whole collection of
them, twenty men and women, were determined to watch
everything I did. It was the sort of examination that you
would not do in public; so I proceeded to put my foot down
and then trouble started. Unless they could all see, he
couldn't stay at the hospital.

"When you come to our hospital you follow the ways of
our hospital. You do not do what you want to do, but you
must follow my ways; I am the doctor."

A long discussion went on among them. In the end I got
my way. We got the man off to the ward, but then came
further strife. James, who called himself the "ward sister,"
insisted that our patient's hair should be cut off because it
was full of mud and earth. Now, the Masai have a habit of
letting their hair grow long, then rubbing into it red mud

nd oil, and having a long braid that goes halfway down
heir back, all daubed with mud and very oily. Our patient
ositively refused to have it off. James positively refused to
eave it there; it would spoil the pillows of his ward, he said.
And so they came to a compromise; the hair would be
arefully tied up inside a hospital sheet. So James got a very
ld sheet, tore it up, and made it into a boudoir cap for this
African. Next piece of friction occurred when James
appeared with a dish to wash our patient, who objected
iolently. "He smells badly," said the "ward sister." He
ertainly had a strange aroma of sour milk and rancid fat.
ames was wrinkling his nose in a most humorous fashion.
n the long run the man *was* bathed, and I made my
xamination, and I found he was in trouble; there was no
oubt about it; he really was in trouble. He needed a minor
peration, and he needed a considerable amount of
nedicine.

I called together all his relations and with the help of
Daudi, explained to them the whole situation, the medicine
e required, what he would have to do, how long he would
tay in the hospital. They listened to it all, and then one of
hem said, *"Acha,"* which is a useful sort of word and
neans, "We won't do it;" or, "Forget it." They had come
or injections; injections they wanted, and only injections.
Jo, they didn't want operations! They wanted injections; if
hey couldn't have injections they would go away!

"Wouldn't it be better to ask the man himself? Is not
his the way of wisdom?"

"Kah," they said among themselves, and then they
sked, "Where is food?"

"What have you got in those gourds, haven't you got your own milk? We have porridge here, you are welcome to share our porridge."

"*Heh,*" they said, disgust on their faces. "Porridge!"

"*Kah,*" said Daudi, getting really warmed up to his subject, "listen, this is a hospital, not a hotel. This is a place where we have medicines that work, and the Bwana here knows what's what. Does the Bwana tell you how to look after your cattle?"

"*Heh,* we should think not. Do we not know all about cattle?"

"Right," said Daudi, "doesn't the Bwana know all about medicine? You follow his way."

This was a new thought to them. They thought for a while, and then they had a talk to their relatives. The talk went on till well after dinner time. When I came up in the early afternoon, I found that they had made their decision. Yes, they realized he had pain, but they were going to follow their own ways. If he couldn't have injections, they wouldn't have anything we could offer.

"*Hongo,*" I said, thinking to myself that we could give him an injection that would pep him up a bit. "I'll give him injections, but you'll have to have the other thing too."

"*Ngh, ngh,*" they shook their heads vigorously, "injection, that's all. That's all we want."

"*Hongo,* what about his trouble? What about his pain?"

"Bwana, give him an injection for it."

"Listen, it doesn't require an injection; it only requires medicine by mouth and a small operation."

"*Ng'o, ng'o,*" they said.

Later in the afternoon Daudi came to me in great concern.

"Bwana, they have gone."

"What, did they leave him behind?"

"No, he has gone, and not only has he gone, Bwana, but he's taken two blankets and a hospital sheet with him."

It was useless to chase after them. They had gone, and if you had reached them, you would have precipitated a lovely fight, which would have meant bloodshed. So I did my best to make what I could out of the difficult situation.

That evening as we were around the campfire, I talked to the dispensers about this topic that was in everybody's mouth.

"Don't you see? He came here with trouble that gives him very bad pain and will eventually destroy his life, but he wanted to be dealt with in his own way; he didn't like the ways of life, he preferred his own way. Behold, he will pay the penalty with his life. But what more could we do? We could offer him the way; we could show him kindness, but unless he followed the only way that would help him, what could we do?"

James was turning over the pages of his New Testament. "Here, Bwana, here are God's words about it. I'll read them to you."

He read from John's gospel. "This is the condemnation, that light is come into the world, and men loved darkness rather than light, because their deeds were evil."

That evening I heard James telling the people in the ward about that story. He said, "If you want to follow God, you follow God at His own terms, not as *you* want to." Then

he told of how the Son of God had died to show just how
God felt about sin, and how His death was the only way ou
for a man to have eternal life.

So although we lost a couple of blankets and a sheet,
felt that it was worth it, because those folk in the ward had
practical sermon that would be told over and over agai
around the campfires in Tanganyika.

14

CHILD TO CHILD

t was one of those ticklish surgical procedures that required
very bit of a doctor's attention.

"Daudi," I whispered, behind the thick mask which
overed my nose and mouth, "hold your breath; this stitch
ust go so deep"—I suited the action to the words—"and
o further. The smallest bit further, and that needle would
e in one of the biggest arteries in the body. Now, here's the
cklish bit; quietly—"

At that moment there was a thunderous bang on the
perating-room door. I stood with the needle poised. "Kefa,
ll those people to be quiet."

I saw my assistant go to the door. There was quietness,
nd the most vital portion of the operation was over before
e door could admit him again.

"Well, who was it?"

"Bwana, it's a woman from the village; she has had four
ildren, all of whom have measles and have been treated by
ur measles squad. Three of her children are very well
deed, but she thinks this one is blind. Bwana, she has
alked fifteen miles today, setting out at *nzogolo* [first
ckcrow]."

"Tell her that I will be there in five minutes, and I'll help
r."

We lifted our patient onto a stretcher and saw hi
carried off to the ward. The woman was standing looki
after the two African dispensers, as they carried t
stretcher along a narrow path, flanked by peanut garden
From the back view I could see a baby held on her bac
piggyback fashion, by an ingenious contraption consisti
of a goatskin and some strips of cloth. Holding her hai
was a little girl three or four years old. Flies swarm
around her eyes, and the child uttered a continual whimpe

"Mbukwenyi [Good morning]," I said.

The woman turned hurriedly, and for two or thr
moments spoke incessantly in a voice full of emotion. T
gist of it was that this child had lost its cough and its co
and her heart was very happy until three days before, wh
she had noticed that the child could not see. I moved over
have a look at the little one. There was a scream from t
child, who buried her face in her mother's side, and when t
mother attempted to sit her on her knee, the child foug
and scratched like a cornered animal and shut her eyelids
tightly that it was impossible to catch even a glimpse of t
eye itself.

"Yah," said the mother, clouting the child on the ba
of the head, "if you don't show the Bwana your eyes at onc
he will eat you."

The child screamed again.

I turned to the mother. "Don't tell the child that; let h
understand that I like her, and that I will not hurt her." A
turning to the little girl I said, "I wouldn't eat you, I li
boys and girls too much, and besides is not porridge the be
kind of food?"

The child opened her eyes the weeniest crack to look at me. At that moment my small son, who was about the same size as the child, came walking up to me, dressed in an abbreviated sunsuit and a topee.

Taking my hand in his he said in Chigogo, "Daddy, what's wrong with that child?"

"Yah," said the little girl, "he speaks our language."

Her eyes opened a little more.

"Yah," she said, "the child is white, all of him."

David went over to her and showed her the various animals on his sunsuit. Child gained the confidence of child and, standing at a distance, I saw her eyes open just sufficiently for me to see two ugly ulcers, each of which, if left, would eat through the clear portion of the eye and leave that poor little African soul blind for life. As the children exchanged confidences, I beckoned to the mother, African-fashion, with the finger upward, but the hand downward and beckoning with all four fingers.

She came over to me, and I whispered, "Don't fear, we will be able to help, but you will have to stay in the hospital with her for perhaps seven days."

"Yoh!" said the woman, "there will be trouble at home. My husband will complain; these are the days when the birds are bad, and we spend very much time saving our crops from them."

"Well, if you wish, leave the child with us, and we will look after her."

"Yoh!" replied the mother, "I could not do that."

"At any rate," I said, "take the child around to the ward, and we will put her to sleep and fix those eyes."

"But Bwana, the child will fight, and you will not be ab‹ to do it."

"Behold, the child will sleep, and while she sleeps, I w‹ treat the ulcers."

I went back into the operating room and took Dav‹ with me.

"David, will you do a little job for me?"

I poured medicine from two bottles carefully into ‹ measuring glass.

"Yes, Daddy," said the youngster in English. "What ‹ I do?"

"Take this to the little girl and ask her to drink it f‹ you."

Carefully I kept out of sight and watched those tw‹ three-year-olds. It was a dramatic moment—the small whit‹ boy and the small black girl. What he said, I did not hea‹ but I saw him take the medicine to her. A small, very dirt‹ black finger was inserted into it. I had carefully put stron‹ syrup with the sedative, and this tickled the child's palate s‹ much that she drank it down greedily, and the little fello‹ came across to me again.

"Daddy, she wants more."

I filled the glass again, this time with pure syrup, bu‹ brought it out myself. Lifting her scarred little eyes the chi‹ said in the most aggressive voice, "I don't want it from you‹ let him give it to me."

I smiled widely and handed it across to my small son‹ who repeated the performance.

"Sit in the sun," I told the mother, "or, if you prefer i‹

the shade of this tree, and let your little one sit on your
nee."

An hour later the little girl was sound asleep, drugged by
e medicine. Gently the mother carried her into the
perating room and the anesthetic was given. Daudi stood
eside me with a number of little bottles and some
harpened matchsticks.

"Hongo," said he, as I washed the eyes out with
ntiseptic solution, "there, Bwana, is what happens to
undreds and hundreds of children. They get measles, they
re not allowed to sleep, their eyes are open all the time,
ey cry until there are no more tears, they rub their eyes,
en the flies get in, and then a little ulcer starts as big as a
in's head, and no one would notice it except us, and then it
ets bigger and bigger, until—"

"Stop there for a moment, Daudi. I'm going to fix *this*
lcer."

I peered at it through a magnifying glass. "It's a
articularly ticklish one, it's deep, so deep that the thickness
f a piece of paper more, and it would be right into the eye."

"Ugh," grunted Daudi.

I took up the sharpened matchstick and just bowing my
ead, I said silently to Almighty God, "O God, guide my
and."

I held my breath and guided that sharpened splinter of
ood with the healing antiseptic on it around the edges of
at ugly crater. I let out a breath.

"Drops, Daudi, please."

These were duly put in and some ointment, and the eye
andaged.

"Oh, you were saying, Daudi, before we started the jo
that the ulcer gets bigger and bigger until—?"

"*Heeh*, Bwana, until it eats right into the eye, and the
comes blindness and often death."

"And yet it starts in such a small way; and unless yc
know what to look for, you wouldn't even notice it."

"True, Bwana, but we do know what to look for, and w
do know how to treat it."

He called the mother, and she picked the child up in he
arms and carried her off to the ward.

As we put away the various medicines and instruments,
said, "Daudi, did you ever understand what that vers
means in God's Book in which it talks about a mote in you
brother's eye, and then a beam in your own?"

The African shook his head. "I don't understand i
Bwana."

"Well, a mote is a very tiny thing. You know when a ra
of light shines through a crack in the door; you see tin
specks in it."

Daudi nodded. "We call that *manhundi hundi*."

"Oh, do you?" I answered. "Well, I'll still prefer to ca
it motes. Tiny little bits, you know how big these tin
little things feel when they are in your eyes."

"*Yah*," said Daudi, "when they are not in your eye the
are tiny. When they are in your eye, they are as big a
nhembo. But, Bwana, what does Jesus mean about th
beam? Is not a beam a big piece of wood?"

I nodded. "That's true. It means this. You must no
have the wrong sort of tongue which criticizes and criticize
and criticizes. Jesus says if you do that, first look for th

very big mistakes and sins in your own life, before you start
trying to get rid of them for other people."

Daudi nodded his head. *"Yah,"* he said, "I think of the
wise words, that unkind criticism is love gone sour."

We walked together to the ward.

"Bwana, this child will see now, and I am going to ask
God to make my eyes clear—the eyes of my soul, I
mean—so that I may help other people and not just
criticize."

15

FIRST SET

Bwana," said the tall Indian, "I should also like some of the white medicine for stomach pains."

We were standing in our hospital dispensary. I nodded to Sila, who was dressed in his best. He filled a bottle with the required white mixture, labeled and corked it, and handed it to the Indian.

"Well, Sulimani, is there anything else we can do for you?"

"Yes, Bwana. I am bringing four of my relations on my return journey in the truck. They have troublesome eyes and require your medicine."

"I will be happy to see them. Now will you be good enough to take Sila to the railway? Behold, he is going on his first visit to the coast. You have never seen the sea before, have you, Sila?"

"No," lisped the African. "I have never theen the thea."

Sulimani and I laughed.

Sila put his hand over his mouth and said, "Don't laugh."

But I couldn't help it, for both this lad's front teeth had been removed by me some months before; and ever since, he had lisped powerfully. A few minutes later we waved good-bye, after I had given Sila full instructions on whom to see here to go, and where to deliver several letters. With a tooting of horns and much shouting, the car left on its way, and I turned back to my office.

Pulling down a book, I turned over to a page marked "Sila." The first entry was made a few years before. I read, "Pneumonia case, carried in, ten days in hospital, sulfapyridine, cost ten shillings." That had been our first contact with this African lad, carried in by Christian relatives; he had had a stiff battle with pneumonia but had reacted dramatically to the sulfa drugs. I remembered how we had made him ward sweeper, while still a convalescent, and how hopelessly clumsy he had been at it. If there was anything upsetable, Sila would upset it!

When he was thoroughly well again, he decided that he would like to be a water carrier; and so for some time he carried two kerosene cans; full of water suspended on a palm pole across his shoulders. With three others, he made fourteen trips a day to the wells a mile and a quarter away, carrying eighty pounds of water on each journey. At first I wondered whether his health would stand it, but the good food of the hospital and the exercise built him up.

It was at this stage I first met his grandfather—a very old man with grizzled curly hair and two of the largest earlobes, loaded with ornaments, that I have ever seen. He came into our hospital complaining of vague pains which he said *jenda jenda* [walked about haphazardly] in his interior. I made my diagnosis and called Sila aside.

"I'm afraid your grandfather will never get better. He has inside him what we call cancer, but if he stays here we can save him from pain and make his passing a kindly one."

The water carrier nodded. He had seen these case before.

"Bwana, it would be well to tell the old man. He is man of courage. He does not fear death."

"Why do you say this?" I asked.

"Well, Bwana, my grandfather was once a well-know witch doctor. He was called 'Mudeko.' He removed ev spirits from people's stomachs and dislodged spells that ha been cast against people."

"How did he do all that?"

At this stage of his career Sila had two front teeth tha stuck out almost at right angles. To call them bucktee would be a gross understatement. They looked like a denta veranda. When he grinned, it could hardly be called a prett sight. But he did grin and said, "Bwana, there are plant known to my grandfather which when cooked with goat' fat will make you very sick indeed. Now, if you thought yo had a spell cast against you and came to my grandfathe paid your fee, a goat or a *debe* [a kerosene can full o flour]—he made his medicine; you swallowed it, and *yah* were you sick! My grandfather had an especially large cla bowl for this part of the proceedings. When you had bee sick, he would put his hand into the bowl."

"Kumbe!" I said, "stop it, that's a disgusting thing t do!"

Sila grinned again, and I shuddered, partly because o the grin and partly because of his grandfather's habits.

"What did he do then?"

"He would find inside it bits of bone, hair, all sorts o things which, of course, he had in his hand first. He woul display these proudly as the cause, and everyone would be happy. But all that, Bwana, was before he heard the words of God. He heard the words of the apostles to the sorcerer. Now, my grandfather had very much money. All day long was he not busy with his medicines and did not people come from great distances for his help? But when he heard the words 'Your money perish with you because you thought that the gift of God may be purchased with money, your heart is not right in the sight of God, repent'—when he heard these words, my grandfather was very upset, and he left his old ways and followed the ways of God."

"Good," I replied, "that's repentance, being sorry enough not to do it again."

Sila nodded. "Therefore, Bwana, seeing that he loves God and follows His ways, why should he fear to die?"

And so it came about that Sila had come more and more into the ward during the final illness of his grandfather. He had been made the hospital hot-water system. He carried out those onerous duties by heating kerosene cans full of water over an open fire and carrying them to the place where they were wanted. He also became a primus expert, always wearing around his neck that most elusive of weapons, a pricker. Upon him had fallen the big job of sterilizing all the instruments in the meningitis epidemic. What a hectic time *that* had been! Cases pouring in and I unable to do the necessary minor operation to diagnose the disease, since I was ill in bed. How I fussed and fretted as I lay there unable even to walk, and then in had come Sila, armed with a couple of test tubes.

108   *Jungle Doctor's Casebook*

"Bwana," said he, "this is the spinal fluid from the tw latest men."

"What?" I replied, clinging to the back of the bed an breathing as well as asthma would allow me. "How did yo collect that?"

Without blinking an eyelid, Sila said, "The usual way with the long needle. Have I not seen you do hundreds; did not just follow the way that you went? Behold, it is a simpl procedure."

That had been the beginning of his taking over quite lot of the hospital work. He had gone on to become a assistant, and later he had learned many of the tricks of doctor. He could diagnose chest complaints quite skillfull and use my stethoscope like a veteran. Over and over again he had diagnosed cases of pneumonia, grinning his far fron lovely grin, and saying, "Behold, Bwana, have I not had thi disease myself; should I not recognize it in others?"

And then came the time when he had become sick vaguely sick, at first with pains here and there. His work had become slipshod, his temper bad. For a very long time, had been at him about his teeth. I had discovered from hi old grandfather that when he was a small boy, in a drunker frenzy, his father had bashed him in the mouth with knobbed stick. The teeth had been loosened; and when th broken jawbone had healed, they had taken on this peculia appearance. Now both of those teeth were dead. I pointed out to him that they were poisoning his system, but no, h refused to have anything done. He lay in the hospital wit his back toward anyone who tried to be sociable, and jus

oped. One day I had come into the ward and heard a
onversation. James, the "ward sister," was talking.

"What good is it, Sila, just to lie there, to make trouble
or yourself and for everybody? Would it not be wiser to
sten to the words of the Bwana?"

"No," rapped Sila. "I won't, I refuse."

"But, listen," said James, "all your trouble will be over,
you get rid of its cause. Has not the Bwana told us how sin
a poison, how it gets right through our souls and weakens
nd makes wretched, and in the end kills our souls? Is not
is poison from your teeth doing the same thing to your
ody."

"Kah," said Sila violently, "go away, go away, *go
way!"*

"But listen," went on James quietly, "you are not a good
itness, a good advertisement for God. You say you believe
a God, and you behave like a small boy."

Sila sat up, furious. But the mere movement of sitting up
aused him to groan.

"Yoh," he groaned, "oh, my back."

"Hongo," said James, "here is the Bwana, he will help
ou."

"Bwana," said Sila, "I have not eaten anything, will you
ot give me a sleep medicine and take these teeth
way—anything?"

Before he could change his mind, I hurriedly boiled up
struments, and half an hour later, the offending teeth were
ut.

"Ah," said James, looking at them, "bad abscesses
deed."

And now a month later Sila was up and about, his o
self again, and on his way to the coast to be the first Africa
from this tribe ever to have false teeth.

16

THE BAD SHEPHERD

Two large animals slunk away, as the headlights of the car focused on them. I stopped, and picking up my large flashlight, got out of the car. In front of us was quite a wide riverbed, and in the middle of it, something vague, that was difficult to see. It was over this that the wild animals had been fighting. I went to investigate. Daudi came behind me, gripping a large stick. Focusing the beam of the light, I saw the carcass of a sheep, one of the fat-tailed variety that live in East Africa. They are thin animals, and the only thing of interest about them is their very fat tails.

"*Heh,*" said Daudi, "*mabisi* [hyenas]. They have been eating a sheep."

"*Hongo,* Daudi, I suppose someone will get into trouble for not having counted his sheep when he brought them back from the pasture."

Daudi nodded. "Bwana, some small boy will be beaten because of that, and rightly too. It is the job of the *mudimi* [shepherd] to look after his sheep, and not to leave any of them out here to be taken by the wild beasts. But, Bwana, perhaps the sheep just died, and it was too far to carry it home for meat."

"*Heh, I* wouldn't like to eat a sheep that died all by itself."

Daudi smiled. "My people don't worry about things lik[e]
that. If they can get meat of any sort, they eat it."

"It's wrong, Daudi; you think! Germs breed ever[y]
twenty minutes. When an animal dies, all sorts of germ[s]
start to eat it up, and they breed very quickly. Ugh! Nasty."

"Then, Bwana," said Daudi, "what happens?"

"A hyena comes along and eats the meat that's full [of]
germs, and then perhaps it bites someone. That's the wors[t]
thing about these animals, these scavengers; they've go[t]
filthy mouths."

Several mornings later, Daudi was assisting me in a[n]
intricate surgical procedure. In the middle of the operatio[n]
Kefa came in, all duly gowned and masked, went behin[d]
Daudi, and whispered something to him. I was too busy a[t]
surgery to take much notice of what was going on.

When the operation was over, Daudi came over to me
and said, "Bwana, you remember the other night, when w[e]
were driving through the moonlight, when we came upon th[e]
dead sheep being eaten by the hyenas?"

I nodded.

"Well, Bwana, there have been a lot of happenings sinc[e]
then."

"How do you mean, Daudi?"

"*Hongo*, Bwana, there was a small boy who was th[e]
shepherd looking after those sheep, and he went and played[.]
His father was very angry with him and beat him. The smal[l]
boy had great anger, and he ran away from his father'[s]
home and went to some of his relations. But on the way i[t]
became dark, and he slept in an old mud hut that had n[o]
door; and as he lay there, in the night, *mbisi* [the hyena]

me and bit his arm. Bwana, it was a very bad bite. The
hall boy screamed in the night, but there was no one to
help him. Through that night he made much noise, but the
noise did not help. The next day he went to his relations,
who took him to the witch doctor. The shoes were thrown,
that the reason for the anger of the spirits might be found;
medicine was made, and a charm put about his neck.
Bwana, it did no good. Behold, he has got worse and worse.
Kefa says that they brought him, and he has put him in the
hospital, his temperature very high; the boy is not talking
the words of wisdom." (By this I knew that Daudi meant he
was delirious.) "And, Bwana, his arm is a very bad arm
indeed."

When I examined the small boy, I realized that whether
it had come through the foul jaws of the hyena, or whether it
had come through the equally foul things the witch doctor
put on sores and injuries, whatever its origin, blood
poisoning had set in, and the small boy's life was in
jeopardy. They had brought him at the very last stages. I did
what I could. Fortunately, in my storeroom I had one of the
sulfa drugs. This drug had a special action on this particular
type of germ.

Quickly we prepared it and gave it. We had to force it
down his throat because of his delirium. We gave him all the
treatment we could, but it was excessively difficult. The arm
was a horrible mess. Once again we dressed the wounds.

James said to me, "Bwana, in our tribal customs,
nobody but a member of his family would touch his arm;
and they would only do it because if they did not, they think
their ancestors would be angry."

James had just finished dressing the arm.

"Well, James, why did you do it? It's against your trib. customs."

"*Mbeka,* truly Bwana, but I've changed my tribe. Am now not one of those who belong to Jesus? Is He not m Chief, and does He not give me orders now? Does He n say, 'So far as you do it unto one of these brothers of Min you do it to Me?' So Bwana, I am doing it for Jesus. When think how His hands were wounded and His feet and H side, I like to feel that I would have had joy to do dressing for His wounds; so I think of this boy, just in the way tha Jesus teaches me to."

Next morning I looked at the lad's chart. Th temperature was still very much up. I felt the only thing t do was inject. We injected.

Once again that evening, things were critical. The arm looked very, very bad. The next morning the temperatur was slightly down; there was some improvement.

James took me aside. "Bwana, during the night he ha been saying strange things. He talks about the way h looked after his sheep. He said he didn't do the wor properly; a bad night, truly, Bwana, but at secon cockcrow, somehow he quietened, and he looks better t me." And better he was, but he seemed to be worried abou what he did not do in looking after his sheep.

"Perhaps, James, it was his father's beating."

"No, Bwana, I think it's because the other boys say t him, 'You're not a good shepherd; you do not watch you sheep.' "

I thought about this the next day when I saw the small boy. Although he was still very sick, he was out of danger.

He said to me, "Bwana, I'm feeling better."

"Good, that's the stuff."

But there was something worrying him. He was only nine, but it was very real to him.

"James, read to him the story from John's gospel, about the good Shepherd. Perhaps that will help him."

One evening I was in the ward, waiting while a plaster was set around the broken arm of another small boy, who was also a shepherd. I talked to these two small folk and told them how Jesus said, "I am the good Shepherd, and I know My sheep and am known of Mine," and how He said that He would look after the sheep. He would keep them from the wild animals. He would not let them perish or let any man pluck them out of His hand.

They listened with the greatest of interest, and then the little hyena-bite lad said, "Bwana, I was not a good shepherd."

"*Kumbe,* you can understand just what it meant to the sheep who couldn't trust you. Don't you think it's a good thing now for you to realize that Jesus wants you to be one of His sheep, and He will never let you down, as you let down your sheep?"

Then I told them that wonderful psalm. It wasn't actually translated into their language, but as well as I could, I translated. I told them that "The Lord is my shepherd, I shall not want."

Others had joined in the group. The hurricane lantern

shone on their faces; and then one of them said to m
"Bwana, these words are of great comfort."

When I came to the verse that said, "Yea, though I wal
through the valley of the shadow of death, I will fear no evi
for thou art with me; thy rod and thy staff they comfo
me," the little boy said, "Bwana, have I not been very clos
to those gates through which no one comes back?"

I nodded. "Yes, old chap."

"Bwana, surely I needed to have Jesus with me then?"

"Truly," I said, "but you need Him more while you a
walking along the path, than when you come to the gates."

"Bwana, I know I need Him."

"Well, what are you going to do?"

"Bwana, do you think if I ask Him, He will make m
one of His sheep?"

I nodded. "There is absolutely no doubt about it."

17

SKIN GRAFT

he only form of lighting we had in our Tanganyikan
ospital was that many-purpose machine, the hurricane
ntern. I turned up the wick a little and hung the lamp on a
ail from one of the roughly cut rafters of our men's ward
oof and set about doing a dressing on a skin graft which I
ad done a week before. I had planned to do the dressing
arlier in the day and knew it would take me at least half an
our, but somehow that half hour had not been
orthcoming. Two operations that I had not expected had
rrived. One of them was a hyena bite.

Now, hyenas are some of the most unclean creatures in
e whole jungle; they are scavengers and will eat anything.
hey have no finer feelings; it is their practice to skulk
ehind the lion and to eat the leftovers of his kill.

One of these brutes had attacked the gardener, Matayo,
nd his arm had been badly bitten.

A bite of this sort could quite easily lead to blood
oisoning and perhaps the loss of a limb, or even the loss of
fe. So I had operated and had done what I could to deal
ith a nasty situation. In the bed behind me lay Matayo,
ropped up on pillows—merely unbleached calico stuffed
ith grass. He was completely out of his anesthetic now,
nd taking a real interest in things. Beside his bed, on a

117

locker, which not long before had been a kerosene can, we
two large white pills and a very large bottle of water.

"Matayo," I said, "I want you to chew up those tw
pills and drink down that water. There are five pints of wat
in that bottle, and you've got to drink one bottleful ever
day."

"*Hongo*," said Matayo, "Bwana, how am I to drin
from so large a bottle with one of my arms all tied up?"

"Look, beside you is a long glass tube. Put that in tⁱ
bottle and suck through it."

He proceeded to do so with gusto. I scrubbed my hanⁱ
thoroughly in a dish that once had been a kerosene can, anⁱ
proceeded to do the dressing.

My patient, a lad of about seventeen, had had a huge lⁱ
ulcer as big as your hand. We had treated it for a long tim
and had given him injections. Then one day, we had take
bits of skin from his other leg and grafted them on. It wa
one of those cases when you would greatly appreciate thⁱ
best type of equipment. However, ancient mosquito nettinⁱ
soaked in liquid paraffin, was the best that we coulⁱ
manage, and his leg had been carefully bandaged for a weeⁱ
I removed those bandages, very carefully bathing the foⁱ
where they had stuck. It was a finicky business, one yoⁱ
couldn't hurry about. My patient craned forward to seⁱ
whether this new work—as he called it—had done any gooⁱ
His relations, among whom was a witch doctor, had scoffeⁱ
at the idea of a man's skin being taken from one leg and puⁱ
on the other. The story of this operation had gone righⁱ
through the country; and Matayo, although he lived fifteeⁱ
miles away, had heard all about it. He was eager to see thⁱ

esult. With my forceps I carefully removed that bandage
bit by bit. Finally, when it was all coiled up in a dish, the
wound lay exposed, and there, looking like islands on a
map, were the skin grafts. They had taken splendidly and
would make that ulcer heal up in three weeks instead of
perhaps three months.

I explained to them just how it all worked.

"Heh," said my patient, "behold, this is a repair work,
Bwana."

Matayo nodded his head. "Truly, it is a repair
work—putting skin from one place to another, like a
gardener moving one plant from one garden to another.
Heh, behold, the doctor can do strange things."

His good hand was lifted to his earlobe, which once had
been so big that you could have easily put a tennis ball in the
vast hole that had been stretched in the lobe; but now it was
just a small thing, so small that you could barely force a
matchstick through the lobe. He had come to me two years
before, saying that he had decided to turn from his tribal
ways to serve God, and he wanted to indicate this to all his
tribesfolk by having his earlobe reduced in size. It appears
that in the days when he was very much a heathen, he had
made much of these earlobes of his, and he felt that it
would be a clear-cut indication of the way that he was going
if he were to have them cut off. His amazement was
tremendous when I said there was no need to do that, as I
could make him a new earlobe which would look like his old
one. With a little bit of surgical fancywork and local
anesthetic and with Matayo auditing proceedings with a
couple of mirrors, he had watched me restore his ears to

something of what they had been before they had been stretched in his youth. His amazement had been tremendous when he saw them appear as they now were.

As he fingered the lobe, he said, "Behold, I did not think it possible that the Bwana could do this work—give me back the ears that I had lost in my youth; but, behold, there are many things that can be done by those who know."

He reached over to his locker and opened with difficulty, with his one good hand, the New Testament in his own language, Chigogo.

"Bwana, let me read to you a verse that explains all this."

"Wait a minute, Matayo, I must first go to the dispensary and get hold of a special sort of ointment that I need for our friend here."

When I came back, Matayo was all ready. He said, "Bwana, listen to these words."

As he read I put a further dressing on that great ulcer and fixed the whole thing up. As I put in the final safety pin Matayo read, "Repent ye therefore, and be converted, that your sins may be blotted out."

"Bwana, that is a verse that helps me to understand."

"How?" I asked.

"*Hongo*, Bwana, it says first of all, 'Repent. Then it says, 'Be converted' so that your sins may be blotted out.'"

"Yes, I agree with that, but how does your ear fit into that?"

"Well, Bwana, you know what to repent means."

Vaguely I groped around in my mind to try and find a decent definition of "to repent." Somehow some of the

nguages that I had learned before I graduated in medicine
eemed to come into focus, and I said, "Yes, I think you
ould say that it means to change your mind."

"*Hah,*" said Matayo, "that's it. To change your mind;
ou decide to go a different way. Did not I decide that I
ould change my ways, did I not come to you and ask you
o change my ears, that I might show the change?"

"Yes, that's true."

Matayo pointed to another word. "It says here, 'Repent
nd be converted.' Now Bwana, to be converted means, to
hange your direction, to go God's way instead of your own.
t means turning completely around."

"True," I said, "true."

"Well, Bwana, when my ears were fixed, did I not try to
urn around and walk God's way?"

"Did you find it easy, Matayo?"

"*Heh,*" he smiled, "did I not find it difficult? But had I
ot God's Book here? And could I not walk to Him day and
ight, whenever I wanted to? Was He not my Father and my
hief?"

I thought of these words as I walked home over the
lains through the darkness of that Central African night,
nd listened to hyenas howling around the place. In the
hickets beyond the mission station, I could hear a grunting
oar, that might have been lion or baboon, and I thought of
he great need of a change of mind and a change of direction
n one's life, if there was going to be that solid contentment
hat comes from knowing that there is no fear beyond the
rave, that there is no fear in life, because you are enlisted in
he army of Almighty God and you are living your life on
His terms.

A week later I was back in that ward. Matayo lay in bed. He looked ghastly. My worst forebodings had been true. His arm had given all the trouble imaginable, and he had lost a tremendous amount of blood through a dangerous hemorrhage. This, fortunately, was controlled. I was giving him a blood transfusion. The blood had been given by the chief of his own village, a man who had been brought up to know about God, and, what is more important, to know God through Matayo's living and everyday practical Christianity in his village.

Once again it was night; once again the lamp hung from its nail; the lad with the skin graft was in bed watching what I was doing to Matayo this time. As I ran the life-giving blood into his veins, Matayo said to me, "Bwana, the Book is over there. There is something I want to read."

"Oh?" I said. "Tell me what the word is."

"Bwana," he said, "it says, 'The blood of Jesus Christ, God's Son, cleanses us from all sin.' *Yah,* behold is not this the blood of the chief of my village that you are running into my arm? Is it not going to give me strength to beat the germs that came into my body through the mouth of the hyena? *Kah,* and is it not the blood of Jesus, God's Son, that comes into the veins of my soul and cleanses out the disease of sin, and makes life forever mine?"

"Matayo, you've got it right. But, behold, God's work is not like mine. I can repair people's legs, but His work is no repair work. It makes us new persons, new creatures."

"*Yah,*" said Matayo, "behold, can we not understand God's Words quite simply, when we apply them to the everyday things of our life?"

18

THE DOG'S TAIL

It was Friday afternoon. The junior dispenser had carefully washed out five kerosene cans. I went to the drawer, pulled out five prescriptions pasted on cardboard, and handed one to each of the dispensers. Samson had a card with the prescription written in proper medical terms and underneath it in the local language, *miti mizeru* [white medicine].

"*Kumbe,*" said Samson, "this week I will bring comfort to many stomachs."

He went across to a great bagful of white powder and took it out.

Daudi's card read "quinine mixture." He smiled and proceeded to weigh out that more than valuable drug in the treatment of malaria, the disease which sweeps thousands into their graves in Central Africa.

"Don't lick your fingers, Daudi," said Samson, "or the medicine will bite you."

The dispensers laughed, and Daudi measured out a teaspoonful of brilliant red dye and added this to his dispensing, for his medicine was called *miti midunghu* [the red mixture].

The two juniors were entrusted with a purple mixture which contained nothing more than bicarbonate of soda and

123

peppermint and was used exclusively for the inquisitive folk who turned up at the hospital "to taste the medicine of the Bwana."

I myself was making the yellow mixture for the folk who had dry coughs. We measured, mixed, stirred, and then poured gallon after gallon of medicine into the huge stockpots which were duly corked and placed on the table. There they sat, all the colors of the rainbow.

"Bwana," said Daudi, "it was a very good thought to color all the medicine differently, and then nobody makes a mistake."

"Are all the tickets in order?" I asked.

A box was brought to me. In it were large square tickets of all colors corresponding with the medicines. If you happened to be large and suffering from indigestion, you got a large dose of white medicine; if you were middle-sized and suffering from malaria, then you received a middle-sized dose of red quinine mixture. If you were small, suffering from rheumatism, then you were presented with a small black ticket, and of course obtained a small dose of black medicine.

Everything was duly put away, and I checked over the whole afternoon's activity. Daudi came across to me.

"Bwana, I have three strangers who would like to see the work of our dispensary. They come from the country way over there." He raised the pitch of his voice and pointed with his chin due north.

"They are members of our tribe, and I met them when I was visiting my relations a week ago. I met them on the

Cape to Cairo road near the signpost which reads, 'To the C.M.S. Hospital, twelve miles.'"*

"Bring them in, we will show them what we do; and Kefa, go and tell my cook, Timothy, to bring a large pot of tea. Tell him I will drink tea with strangers, and therefore supply enough sugar!"

Kefa scampered off.

Looking around rather furtively, my visitors came in. They were typical African tribesmen, and as striking a cross section of the tribe of the Wagogo as you could ask. The leader was an old man with grizzled curly hair, and a few straggling white bristles sprouting from the chin. His cheekbones were ornamented (it's all a matter of taste!) with deep scars that radiated out beneath his eyes; his ears had been stretched so that they would reach halfway down to his shoulders, and they contained a safety pin and a selection of bead ornaments. His chest was bare; he was dressed in a black cloth tied around his middle, while his feet were protected from the roughness of the ground by cowhide sandals. Beside him was a young warrior, mud in his hair and a pigtail two feet long, made from fiber and red mud, trailing down his back. He had a cloth knotted over one shoulder, and he strode along with the easy lope of one who finds a forty-mile walk in one day quite within his scope. He was armed with a six-foot spear, razor-sharp. The third was a youth, dressed in a dirty pair of shorts and carrying a knobbed stick.

I duly greeted these folk, African fashion, going through the long rigmarole of greeting, and then invited them to sit

---

*C.M.S. stands for the Church Missionary Society, the jungle doctor's mission board.

down on stools in the dispensary. They looked at all th
medicines we had just made.

"*Yah,*" said one, "*yali yehwanile mchila lya mbwa.*"

I translated this into English. "This medicine is like th
tail of a dog."

"Daudi," I said, "that's a new one on me; I cannot se
any dogs' tails in that anywhere."

The head dispenser threw back his head and laughe
cheerfully. "Bwana, our people call the rainbow 'the tail o
the dog.' "

"*Hongo,* I see, but why the *tail* of the dog?"

"It's just called the tail of a dog, Bwana. Perhaps be
cause when it comes, the rains goes; perhaps because dog
tails are curved; I don't know."

I turned to the Africans again. "These are the medicine
that we make for the sick."

"*Yah,*" said the old man, "*nda yangu yikuluma* [m
stomach bites these days]."

Kefa raised his eyebrows.

I nodded. "Give him some of the white medicine."

The old man drank a glassful noisily, ran his tongu
around his lips, and said, "*Yoh,* that's medicine!"

"It is indeed," said Daudi, "do we not see man
hundreds of people every week whose stomachs bite? Bu
this medicine will break the teeth of any stomach."

And then of course the other two wanted to test it also
This they duly did, and I had the greatest difficulty i
stopping them from having a sip of all the various an
variegated bottles that were in front of me.

"Bwana," said Daudi, "I met these folk over by th

ost. They asked me where the road went; so I told them;
nd as we walked here I told them of the signpost of life,
ow Jesus talked to people and said, 'I am the way, the truth
nd the life; no man comes to the Father but by Me,' and I
old them that while there were many ways to our hospital,
here was only one way to God."

The oldest man broke in. "But Bwana, we did not be-
ieve him. He told us of things that could not happen, of
nen who had the disease of death [meningitis] and who got
etter because of medicine that you gave to them, of men
vho had been blind for years and who could see again after
oming to the hospital."

The young warrior nodded his head till his pigtail waved
langerously. "Truly," he said, "and he told us of ulcers as
oig as your hand that disappeared with injections." (He used
he word for when people are stabbed.)

"Well," I replied, "and did he prove it?"

"*Yah*," said the old man, "my eyes were opened. We
valked through the village and he said, 'Come and I will
how you a man.' And out came a young and strong man
ike my son here." (He pointed with his chin toward the
oossessor of the pigtail.) "Daudi spoke to him and said,
Tell them about the disease of death.'

" '*Yah*,' said the young man, 'my relations thought I
vas dead; my neck was stiff, my body was stiff, my head
iched, and my wisdom had departed. I remember lying in
ny house here, and then I found myself in a bed; and behold
ny back was very sore, as though I had fallen into a
hornbush; and behold, I was hungry, and soon I was home
igain and well. All because they had the right medicine over

there, and he pointed, Bwana, to the hill where this hospita
is. So Daudi said to me, 'There, the disease of death i
beaten with the right medicine.' Then we came to anothe
village, and I met an old man whom I knew. His name wa
Mesomabi [Bad Eyes]. Had he not been blind for years, di
he not grope around the place until he came here, and yo
worked on his eyes? Bwana, I knew that man was blind. H
had tried every witch doctor, every way, and it was only yo
who could help him."

"*Heh,*" said Daudi, "he met women whose children ha
all died, till they came to our hospital. He saw men wit
healed ulcers, men whose teeth had been pulled out withou
pain; and now he's going to stay in Mvumi that he may lear
of the other side of our work."

I nodded. "It is not effective to grow thornbush around
leopard," I said. "It's better to kill it."

The old man nodded.

"We don't just make your sickness better, but we try t
take from you the sting that's behind them all, the fear o
death, the fear of evil."

The man shivered.

"Daudi will tell you," I went on, "as he told you on th
way. There is only one road, and he and these of your ow
tribe will tell you the Way to God. It's the way of a man,
man who is the Son of God."

At that moment the tea arrived, and a noisy quarter o
an hour ensued.

As I left them the old man said, "May I come to th
hospital each day, Bwana, to hear these words which speak
of good news?"

"Certainly, great one, that's what our hospital is for."